Maths Action Plans

Solving Problems and Handling Data

Y5/P6

David Clemson and Wendy Clemson

⇨ Contents

Autumn term

Introduction

Maths Action Plans (MAPs) is a series of practical teacher's resource books, four for each year of the primary school from Year 3/P4 to Year 6/P7. Each book contains lesson plans designed to help you to plan and deliver well-structured lessons in line with the National Numeracy Strategy *Framework for Teaching Mathematics* (1999).

MAPs is different from other lesson-plan based resource books because each title in the series focuses upon a different strand of mathematics at a particular year, thereby offering you a more coherent, "joined-up" approach to the teaching of key mathematical concepts. The activities in this book cover the following mathematical topics within the "Solving problems" and "Handling data" strands:

- problems involving "real life", money and measures (including time)
- organising and interpreting data.

While the lessons are designed to offer support across a strand, links to other strands are made clear throughout. For example, "Using and applying mathematics" underpins all three National Curriculum attainment targets. There are three aspects of "using and applying" covered by the contents of this book:

- problem solving
- communicating
- reasoning.

Within each aspect, children have to:

- organise
- select/decide
- explain/justify
- make connections
- try different approaches.

The MAPs lessons will encourage the children to organise their thinking about problems, select appropriate operations, explain their reasoning and suggest alternative methods. Lessons addressing other strands in the mathematics curriculum, that is "Measure, Shape and Space"; "Number" and "Calculations", can be found in companion titles in this series.

Planning – adopting or adapting

Although these books focus on specific mathematics topics, they also offer a bank of lessons that give complete coverage in line with the *Framework for Teaching Mathematics Sample Medium Term Planner* (2000). Every objective is tackled and the number of lessons matches the number of lessons in the planner exactly. This means that MAPs can be used as a complete core mathematics programme. Alternatively, the lessons can be used as additional plans for an existing scheme of work. Where fresh ideas or alternative approaches are desired then the lessons in MAPs can fit the bill.

To adapt or personalise the MAPs lessons to meet your needs, you might consider the following actions:

- select and copy individual MAPs lessons or units to supplement lessons/units that you have already
- add your own prepared resources to those recommended in the plans
- check that the lessons match the needs of children in your class and if necessary substitute lessons for MAPs lessons from other years for more or less confident children
- work on the first lessons of a unit, then plan the use of supplementary activities as a stimulus for extension work or as the starting points for subsequent whole-class lessons.

The intention throughout is to provide fresh ideas for planning the content, pace and pitch of your lessons within a framework that can be adopted or adapted to meet your needs and the needs of your class.

Curriculum planner

The lessons in this book have been written in line with the *Framework for Teaching Mathematics Sample Medium Term Planner* (2000).

The opening page of each unit includes the following information, which can be used in your medium term plans:

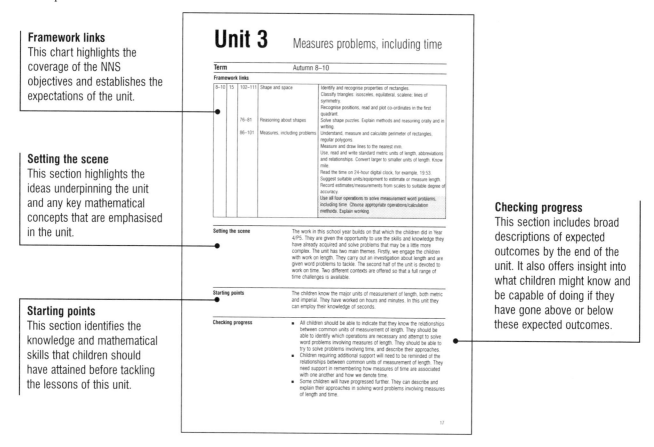

Framework links
This chart highlights the coverage of the NNS objectives and establishes the expectations of the unit.

Setting the scene
This section highlights the ideas underpinning the unit and any key mathematical concepts that are emphasised in the unit.

Starting points
This section identifies the knowledge and mathematical skills that children should have attained before tackling the lessons of this unit.

Checking progress
This section includes broad descriptions of expected outcomes by the end of the unit. It also offers insight into what children might know and be capable of doing if they have gone above or below these expected outcomes.

For each topic area, the MAPs have been carefully planned to ensure that lessons meet the requirements of teachers in Scotland and Wales given in the attainment targets both for *National Guidelines 5–14* in Scotland and in *Mathematics in the National Curriculum in Wales*. A correlation chart for *National Guidelines 5–14* in Scotland is presented on page viii. A correlation chart for *Mathematics in the National Curriculum in Wales* can be accessed on the following website: www.nelsonthornes.com/primary

Differentiation

MAPs offers a controlled level of differentiation as the National Numeracy Strategy recommends. This can be by task, through assessed outcomes and/or suggestions for planning on the basis of prior knowledge or experience. In some cases whole-class lessons are offered with "escape points"; in other cases there are lessons with differentiated resource sheets or lessons where "support" or "challenge" ideas offer an alternative route for individuals, pairs or groups.

Assessment

The learning objectives for each lesson are clearly stated and assessment opportunities are offered throughout in many of the pupil activities and resource sheets. Make time to observe the children as they work at these tasks during the main part of the lesson. Identify whether children have understood the concept or whether they have any misconceptions that need to be addressed. You might, at this stage, plan the use of additional support or challenge materials identified in each plan.

During the plenary, key questions are offered to provide important assessment information to guide teaching and planning. These should be supplemented by the use of open questions such as *How did you work that out?*, *What if … ?* and *Are there other ways of working this out?*

Finally, for medium term assessment, additional tasks can be planned for individual pupils or small groups during the half-termly "assess and review" lessons by using pupil activities or the supplementary activities at the end of each unit.

The MAPs lesson

The plans are intended as a support for the daily mathematics lesson for the school mathematics co-ordinator, teacher and classroom assistant working within a particular group. Each lesson includes the following sections:

Learning objectives
This section gives the explicit targets for each lesson including oral and mental starters.

Mental/oral starter
This shows the balance of oral and mental objectives across each title. Some are free-standing, others link to the main activity.

Main activity
Detailed guidance is given here which covers the main part of each lesson, including a description and organisation of the activity and a range of ideas for differentiating each lesson. Key questions are highlighted in italics.

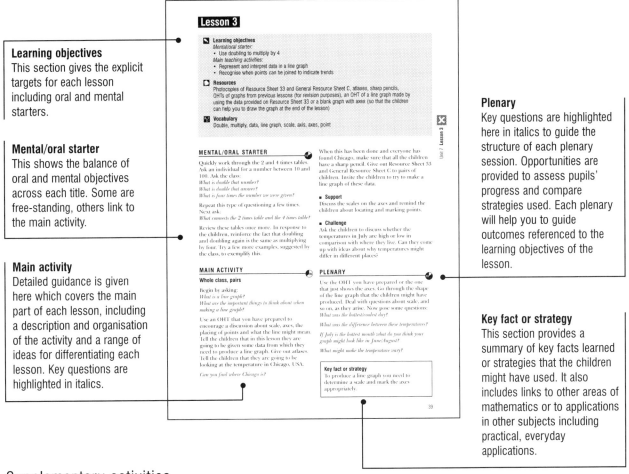

Plenary
Key questions are highlighted here in italics to guide the structure of each plenary session. Opportunities are provided to assess pupils' progress and compare strategies used. Each plenary will help you to guide outcomes referenced to the learning objectives of the lesson.

Key fact or strategy
This section provides a summary of key facts learned or strategies that the children might have used. It also includes links to other areas of mathematics or to applications in other subjects including practical, everyday applications.

Supplementary activities

Fresh ideas are provided here, with further exemplification, different approaches, homework opportunities ...

Homework
Weekly homework opportunities are described here, covering the objectives of the unit.

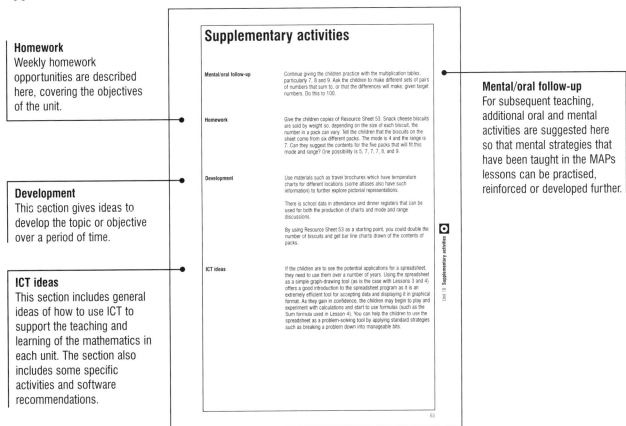

Mental/oral follow-up
For subsequent teaching, additional oral and mental activities are suggested here so that mental strategies that have been taught in the MAPs lessons can be practised, reinforced or developed further.

Development
This section gives ideas to develop the topic or objective over a period of time.

ICT ideas
This section includes general ideas of how to use ICT to support the teaching and learning of the mathematics in each unit. The section also includes some specific activities and software recommendations.

Scottish correlations

In this curriculum planner chart, no reference has been made to the activity at the beginning of each lesson in this book, namely the mental/oral starter. These are designed to augment the numeracy and mathematical understanding of the children. They are wide-ranging and often address different objectives from those set down for the main activities of each lesson. It is possible for teachers in Scottish schools to select from the mental/oral starters those which match their pupils' learning and teaching needs.

Additionally, at the end of each unit of this book there are supplementary activities, and suggestions for using ICT. These will support work related to the Information Handling Target and the Number, Money and Measurement Attainment Target.

Scottish guidelines planner

Information handling attainment targets		
Strands	**Level C**	**Level D**
Collect		Select information sources *Unit 2*
Organise		Use diagrams or tables *Unit 2* Use a database or spreadsheet table *Unit 10*
Display	Construct a bar graph *Unit 2*	Construct graphs *Units 7, 10*
Interpret	From displays and databases – retrieve *Unit 2*	From a range of displays and databases – retrieve subject to one condition *Unit 10*

Number, money and measurement attainment targets		
Strands	**Level C**	**Level D**
Money	Use coins/notes to £5 *Unit 1*	UK coins/notes to £20 plus, exchange *Units 1, 4, 5, 8*
Add and subtract	Applications in number, measurement, money to £20 *Units 1, 3, 4, 5, 6, 8, 9, 11, 12*	Applications in number, measurement, money *Units 4, 5, 6, 9, 11, 12*
Multiply and divide	Applications in number, measurement, money to £20 *Units 3, 4, 5, 6, 8, 9, 11, 12*	Applications in number, measurement, money *Units 4, 5, 6, 9, 11, 12*
Time		24 hour timetables *Unit 11*

Unit 1 — Money and "real-life" problems

Term	Autumn 2–3

Framework links

2–3	10	52–57	Understanding × and ÷	Understand the effect of and relationships between the four operations, and the principles of arithmetic laws as they apply to multiplication.
				Use doubling or halving: double any two-digit number;
		60–65	Mental calculation strategies (× and ÷)	Halve an even number, double the other; to multiply by 25, multiply by 100 then divide by 4;
				Multiply by 16 × 8, then double; find a ⅙ by halving a ⅓. Approximate first.
		66–69	Pencil and paper procedures (× and ÷)	Use informal pencil and paper methods to support, record or explain × and ÷.
				Extend written methods to HTU × U or U.t × U.
		82–85	Money and "real-life" problems	Use all four operations to solve money or "real-life" word problems.
		70–75	Making decisions and checking results including using a calculator	Choose appropriate operations/calculation methods. Explain working. Check by estimating. Use inverse operation.

Setting the scene

During Year 4/P5 the children will have had several opportunities to work with word problems involving numbers and money. More opportunities are given in Year 5/P6. The children should begin to become adept at explaining their working out and also practise further their estimating skills. They begin to use inverse operations and/or equivalent calculations to check their work. In Unit 1 we use the context of "camping" to generate a variety of realistic money problems and challenges.

Starting points

The children already know how to read a story problem carefully, interpret the operation or operations necessary to solve it and carry through addition, subtraction, multiplication and/or division to find a solution. They should be able to solve one-step and multi-step problems in this way. They have begun to talk through their methods and use approximation to check their answers.

Checking progress

- All children should be able to solve one-step and simple multi-step money and number problems, involving all four operations, and talk about how they did them. They should know what estimating is and make estimates of answers.
- Children requiring additional support should cope with one step problems, and, with support, work through multi-step problems.
- Some children will have progressed further and be able to solve, unaided, a wide range of money and number problems. By using estimation they can make checks on their work.

Lesson 1

◤ Learning objectives

Mental/oral starter:
- Round three-digit numbers to the nearest 10
- Round three-digit numbers to the nearest 100
- Round four-digit numbers to the nearest 10
- Round four-digit numbers to the nearest 100

Main teaching activities:
- Use addition, subtraction, multiplication and division to solve money problems
- Explain how they worked them out
- Check answers by estimating

📖 Resources

A bank of numbers to draw on to yield numbers for rounding (These can be from a data list, a list of random numbers or a telephone directory. A sample is shown below, taken from the postcode list in a telephone directory. The initial "0" can be omitted when the numbers are used.), photocopies of Resource Sheet 1, photocopies of Resource Sheet 2, OHTs of both resource sheets

(Note: As an additional resource for children who require extra support, the images on Resource Sheet 1 can be enlarged and photocopied separately for mounting on card. The children can then lay in front of them the items that they need.)

🔤 Vocabulary

Add, subtract, multiply, divide, operation, check, estimate

MENTAL/ORAL STARTER

Tell the children that you would like them to round some numbers to the nearest 10. Call out some three-digit numbers from your number bank. Here is an example pool of numbers from which digits can be read.

Pocklington **01759**	Porthcawl **01656**	Ramsbottom **01706**
Polegate **01323**	Porthmadog **01766**	Ramsden **01993**
Polmont **01324**	Porthtowan **01209**	Ribchester **01254**
Polperro **01503**	Portishead **01275**	Richards Castle **01584**
Polruan **01726**	Puddletown **01305**	Richhill **028 38**
Pomeroy **028 87**	Pulborough,	Richmond,
Pontardawe **01792**	W. Sussex **01798**	N. Yorks **01748**
Pontardulais **01792**	Pulham Market **01379**	Rickmansworth **01923**
Pontefract **01977**	Pumpsaint **01558**	Ridgeway Cross **01886**
Ponteland **01661**	Puncheston **01348**	Ridgewell **01440**
Ponterwyd **01970**	Purfleet **01708**	Ridgmont **01525**
Pontrhydfendigaid **01974**	Puriton **01278**	Rillington **01944**
Pontrhydygroes **01974**	Pwllheli **01758**	Ringford **01557**
Pontshaen **01545**	Pymoor **01353**	Ringmer **01273**
Pontyates **01269**		Ringwood **01425**
Pontyberem **01269**	**Q**	Ripe **01323**
Pontybodkin **01352**	Quatt **01746**	Ripley, Derbys **01773**
Pontycymmer **01656**	Queens Head **01691**	Ripon **01765**
Pontypool **01495**	Quidenham **01953**	Risca **01633**
Pontypridd **01443**	Quorn **01509**	Roade **01604**
Poole **01202**		Roadhead **01697 7**
Poolewe **01445**	**R**	Robertsbridge **01580**
Pooley Bridge **01768 4**	Raasay **01478**	Rocester **01889**
Porlock **01643**	Rackenford **01884**	Rochdale **01706**
Portadown **028 38**	Radcliffe-on-Trent (6)	Rockbourne (6) **01725**
Portaferry **028 427**	**0115 9**	Rockcliffe,
Port Askaig **01496**	Radcliffe-on-Trent (7)	Cumbria **01228**
Portavogie **028 427**	**0115**	Rockcliffe,
Port Charlotte **01496**	Radlett **01923**	Kirkcudbright **01556**
Port Dinorwic **01248**	Radwinter **01799**	Rockingham **01536**
Port Ellen **01496**	Radyr, S. Glam **029 20**	Rock,
Port Erin,	Raglan **01291**	Kidderminster **01299**
Isle of Man **01624**	Rainford **01744**	Rogart **01408**
Port Glasgow **01475**	Rainham, Essex **01708**	Rogate, W. Sussex **01730**
Portglenone **028 25**	Rait **01821**	Romford, Essex **01708**
Porth **01443**	Rampton **01777**	Romsey, Hants **01794**

Do this exercise for at least 15 numbers. Ask individual children for the answers. Repeat the exercise by asking for the numbers to be rounded to the nearest 100.

Use four-digit numbers and repeat the whole exercise. If a telephone directory code list is used, the initial '0' can be omitted and then the number read forwards or backwards, or the digits can be jumbled up. The number 0 1273, for example, gives 1273, 3 721, 2 731, 7 321, 3 127, 3 271 and 3 712.

MAIN ACTIVITY

Whole class, pairs

Show the children the OHT of Resource Sheet 1. Talk through the items and prices. Tell the children that this lesson and the next two lessons will draw on the experiences of Gail and John on Scout camp. Show the OHT of Resource Sheet 2 to the children and talk through challenges 1 and 3. Discuss how they might be tackled.

Give out copies of Resource Sheets 1 and 2 to pairs of children. Allow them to work through the challenges on Resource Sheet 2 and set out their answers in the boxes provided.

■ **Support**

Offer support to the children who find the challenges difficult by working through the first one with them. Allow them to do the second. Do the next one together. Continue supporting in this way throughout the session.

■ **Challenge**

Ask the pairs of children who complete the challenges to write down how they can make an estimate which checks their answer. In response to the first puzzle, they may say:

Drinking chocolate costs nearly £1 and 6 eggs nearly £1. My estimate would be that they cost close to £2, so they could easily be bought for less than £3.

PLENARY

Take examples from each section of Resource Sheet 2 and work them through with the children. Make estimates to check the answers obtained.

> **Key fact or strategy**
> Follow through a problem a step at a time.

Lesson 2

 Learning objectives

Mental/oral starter:
- Addition facts for each number up to 20
- Subtraction facts for each number up to 20

Main teaching activities:
- Use addition, subtraction, multiplication and division to solve multi-step money problems
- Explain how they worked them out
- Check answers by estimating

 Resources

Photocopies of Resource Sheets 1 and 3, small whiteboards and pens

Vocabulary

Add, subtract, multiply, divide, operation, check, estimate

MENTAL/ORAL STARTER

Write a number between 1 and 20 on the board. Invite the children to complete the "fan" of numbers that can be summed to give this number. Here is an example.

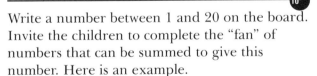

Write up the same number and work on subtraction bonds from 10 and 20. Here are those starting with 10.

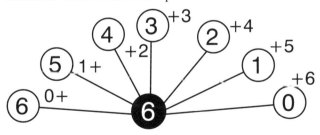

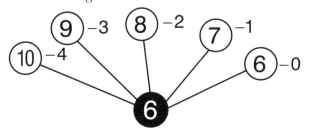

Take another number and ask the children to call out the sequence of bonds or write them on their own white boards. Try this with a selection of numbers in turn.

MAIN ACTIVITY

Whole class, individuals, pairs

Remind the children of the shopping work they have done relating to Gail and John preparing for Scout camp. Explain that in this lesson they should work out the costs of Gail's and John's shopping lists. Give a copy of Resource Sheets 1 and 3 to each child. They will also need rough paper and their exercise books.

■ **Support**

The children will need an expanded form of the shopping list. Thus Gail's list should read:
8 tins baked beans ... the cost of 4 tins is ..., the cost of 8 tins is ...; 10 kg potatoes ... the cost of 5 kg potatoes is ..., the cost of 10 kg potatoes is ..., and so on.

3

■ Challenge

Those who need a further challenge can make up a shopping list of their own to include a wider variety of items but not costing more than, say, £20.

PLENARY

Discuss with the children the ways they worked out the shopping lists, and what their conclusions were. Discuss what estimates one might reach to help in checking the answers.

> **Key fact or strategy**
> Estimates help us to establish whether our answers are correct.

Lesson 3

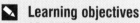

◥ Learning objectives

Mental/oral starter:
- Add any pair of two-digit numbers
- Subtract any pair of two-digit numbers

Main teaching activities:
- Use addition, subtraction, multiplication and division to solve word problems (employing single- and multi-step methods)
- Use addition, subtraction, multiplication and division to solve money problems (employing single- and multi-step methods)
- Explain how they worked them out
- Check answers by estimating

📖 Resources

Photocopies of Resource Sheets 4 and 5, a list of two-digit numbers

🔤 Vocabulary

Add, subtract, multiply, divide, operation, check, estimate

MENTAL/ORAL STARTER

Use the prepared list of two-digit numbers or the number ladder on Resource Sheet 5 to call out pairs of numbers and ask the children to add them together. The number ladder will be re-used as a resource for the mental/oral follow-up.

Call out pairs of numbers and invite the children to take the lower number from the higher one.

MAIN ACTIVITY

Whole class, individuals, small groups

Give a copy of Resource Sheet 4 to each child and talk it through. Give the children a short while to work on the challenges. When they complete, they can join in groups to explain to one another how they did the calculations and what estimates helped them to check their answers.

■ Support

The children should be taken carefully through each challenge. Once it is decided which operations are required, the children should try the arithmetic for themselves.

■ Challenge

What happens to the calculations if the minibuses hold not 15 but 18 people, and each bus costs £45 rather than £39?

PLENARY

Discuss with the class some of the methods in use, the kinds of calculations required and appropriate estimates.

> **Key fact or strategy**
> Estimation is a good checking tool.

Supplementary activities

Mental/oral follow-up

Invite the children to cut up the number ladders on Resource Sheet 5. They should then lay any two ladders alongside one another as shown here.

The children can work out the answers to the resulting additions and subtractions, or quiz a partner about the answers to these.

71	
14	
36	
48	
86	
16	
52	
76	63
28	43
44	82
90	11
56	92
38	64
	22
	50
	19
	34
	44
	75
	42

number in use

76 + 63

43 – 28

44 + 82

90 – 11

92 – 56

38 + 64

Homework

Give the children a fresh list of data about a Guide, Brownie, Scout or Beaver camp. They can then create either a camp shopping list or four story challenges involving people or events at camp. These can be shared with the class.

Development

Use Resource Sheet 1 to create a new price list for all the items. Shopping lists and other challenges can be created by using the new prices.

Use a food shopping catalogue (like those produced by supermarkets). Ask the children to make up a provision list of their own from the authentic items and prices. Their lists can be used in a new set of challenges.

ICT ideas

Check out the Ambleside school web site at:
http://ambleweb.digitalbrain.com/ambleweb/web/Games/
The site contains a constantly updated selection of maths games and puzzles. Recent additions include "Button Beach Challenge", in which children have to work out the value of various coloured buttons on a grid.

GridClub, the online project for 7–11 year olds, at
http://www.gridclub.com also contains many appropriate interactive games and puzzles.

Unit 2 Handling data

Term				Autumn 6	

Framework links

6	8	112–117	Handling data	Discuss chance or likelihood. Present and interpret data on a bar chart and bar line graph: axis in 2s, 5s, 10s, 20s, 100s. Recognise when intermediate points have no meaning. Make a simple database on paper. Identify the mode.

Setting the scene

Chance is central to all of our lives. We weigh up the possibilities of crossing the road safely, of getting a new job or of winning the national lottery. In this unit we explore many facets of chance and the probabilities we can attribute to events. It is important to understand that there is often a distinction between theoretical odds and practical outcomes. Understanding the difference between theoretical and experimental results is quite sophisticated. We can begin the process of encouraging the children to gain insights into the difference.

The use of simple likelihood lines is a good way to explore the central ideas on which probability and chance are based. We have a sense of what is likely in our everyday lives as well as a sense of fairness. Children are very strong in their views about what is possible and fair, particularly in relation to the actions of adults. Whilst we do not commonly engage in mathematical analysis when making everyday decisions about right or wrong, fair or unfair, it is important that the children see fairness as an appropriate topic in mathematics. To explore further ideas of likelihood, probability and chance, the lessons in this unit support exploration of possible outcomes.

In addition to understanding probabilities it is important to be able to present data in charts and to be able to read and interpret such charts. After our work on chance, we explore bar charts and bar line graphs. Some basic work on databases is developed and calculators are used where appropriate.

Starting points

Children should have some experience of playing board and card games. Prior to the first lesson, give the children further experiences with games such as "Snakes & Ladders", "Junior Scrabble", simple card games, and dominoes. In earlier years the children will have worked on simple pictorial representation, data collection and simple analysis.

Checking progress

- All children should be able to discuss "fair" and "unfair" in broad terms. They should know about tallying, pictograms, and simple bar charts and block graphs.
- Children requiring additional support will need lots of examples of likely and unlikely events. They will need reminding about the rules for setting out bar charts.
- Some children will have progressed further and will be able to make sensible statements about relative probabilities. They will be able to use their understanding of bar charts in working with bar line graphs.

Lesson 1

Learning objectives
Mental/oral starter:
• Read and write whole numbers to 100 000
Main teaching activity:
• Discuss chance or likelihood

Resources
Examples of games (Include some that the children have played prior to the lesson.), coins, dice, hexagonal spinners (General Resource Sheet A can be used), calculators

Vocabulary
Fair, unfair, chance, likely, likelihood, probable, digit

MENTAL/ORAL STARTER

Give a calculator to each pair of children. Ask one child in each pair to key in a number with four digits. They then give the calculator to their partner who says the number in the display. Invite a few individuals to write and say the numbers for the whole class. When the children are confident with four-digit numbers, ask them to key in five digits and look and say. Sample different pairs so that they can share their numbers with the whole class. Collect in the calculators.

MAIN ACTIVITY

Whole class, pairs or small groups

Show the children some of the games that you have assembled.

Is this a fair game?

What do we mean by "luck"?

Can any of these games be won without luck?

Explore responses. Encourage the children to see that some games, such as "Snakes & Ladders", are based on chance. Others, like "Scrabble", need some luck but also need skill. Write on the board any words used that relate to chance and discuss what they mean.

Toss a coin and ask:
What can I get?

Explain that with a coin there are just two possible outcomes.
Can you think of other things where there are just two possible outcomes?

There are few of these. Examples include babies being either boys or girls, and whole numbers being either odd or even.

Give out coins or dice and/or hexagonal spinners to pairs or small groups. Ask the children to either write "Heads" and "Tails" at the head of two columns or "1 to 6" (inclusive) in a row on a piece of paper. If coins are used, tell the children that you want them to toss the coin at least twenty times and tally the number of heads and tails they get. If dice or spinners are used, they should roll the dice or spin the spinner at least fifteen times and make a tally of the results.

■ Support
Some children may need help with organising the data collection. A reminder about tallying may be necessary. Coin tossing may need practice.

■ Challenge
Some children, if using dice or spinners, might go on to look at the distribution of all of the numbers. Are there the same number of 1s, 2s, 3s, 4s, 5s and 6s? Would we expect this? If there are not, can they think why this might be so?

PLENARY

Make a table on the board for Heads and Tails or for Odds and Evens. Ask each pair or group that tossed a coin to tell you their total of heads and tails. Ask groups or pairs that worked with dice or spinners to give you totals of even numbers and odd numbers that were thrown. Write down the totals for each pair in two columns.

Do you think that when we add up the columns they ought to be the same?

Ask for help to do the sum and then ask:
Are they the same?

If not, ask why this might be the case. Remind the children that there is an even chance for every toss or throw. Explain that when we do an experiment like this chance can mean that we do not always get equal outcomes.

Key fact or strategy
There are just a few things in life that have only two possible outcomes. Every time that a coin is tossed there is an equal chance that heads or tails will be the result and with dice there is an even chance that an odd or an even number will be thrown.

Lesson 2

 Learning objectives
Mental/oral starter:
• Round any three or four-digit number to the nearest 10 or 100
Main teaching activity:
• Discuss chance or likelihood

 Resources
Four ballot boxes labelled "Certain", "Likely", "Unlikely" and "Impossible", Resource Sheet 6, scissors

Vocabulary
Round, certain, likely, unlikely, impossible, chance, likelihood

MENTAL/ORAL STARTER

Ask the children to tell you some three-digit numbers and get them to write these on the board. For each one ask what the number would be to the nearest 10 and then the nearest 100. Use this opportunity to review the rules we use in rounding. Repeat this procedure for some four-digit numbers.

MAIN ACTIVITY

Whole class, small groups

Show the children the four boxes and the labels that you have prepared. Ask what each of the terms means. Now offer some statements and ask the children to tell you which statement might be put in which box. Examples of statements are:

1 It will get dark tonight.
2 I will watch TV tonight.
3 The centre of the Earth is filled
   with ice-cream.
4 It will snow on Christmas Day.
5 I will grow taller than Mum.

Discuss the decisions taken. Where there are differences of view, explain that this does not mean that one person is necessarily wrong, for example, some children may not have TV at home.

Give out Resource Sheet 6 and scissors to small groups. Ask the groups to cut the sheet into five statements and then decide as a group in which ballot box they want to post each one. Where there is disagreement either allow more than one vote or ask the group to consider the statement as being for all of them, for example, it is unlikely that all the group will play Premier League football. As groups are ready they should post the statements in the appropriate boxes.

■ **Support**
Read through the statements, as necessary, to make sure everyone comprehends exactly what is meant by each.

■ **Challenge**
Ask children to prepare four statements, one for each of the ballot boxes.

PLENARY

Read out sample statements from each box. Ask whether the class agrees that they were in the correct box. Discuss why a statement is seen as certain ... why another is unlikely, and so on.

Key fact or strategy
The likelihood of something happening can vary according to personal circumstances and knowledge.

Lesson 3

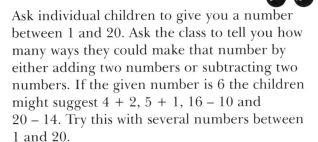

Learning objectives
Mental/oral starter:
• Recall addition and subtraction facts for each number up to 20
Main teaching activity:
• Discuss chance or likelihood

Resources
Resource Sheet 7, Resource Sheet 8, an OHT of a likelihood scale or a drawing of this on the board (like the one on Resource Sheet 8)

Vocabulary
Addition, subtraction, certain, more likely, less likely, good chance, even chance, poor chance, no chance, likelihood

MENTAL/ORAL STARTER

Ask individual children to give you a number between 1 and 20. Ask the class to tell you how many ways they could make that number by either adding two numbers or subtracting two numbers. If the given number is 6 the children might suggest 4 + 2, 5 + 1, 16 – 10 and 20 – 14. Try this with several numbers between 1 and 20.

MAIN ACTIVITY

Small groups, whole class, small groups

Give copies of Resource Sheet 7 to small groups. Ask the children to discuss each statement and decide how likely it is to be true. When the children are ready, go through the sheet and get the views of different groups. Show the children a likelihood scale (either one drawn on the board or by using the overhead projector). Use some of the items on Resource Sheet 7 to help the children to see how to use such a scale. Give out Resource Sheet 8. Ask each group to work through it and place statements on the scale by using the number of each statement.

■ Support

Remind the children of the work they did in the last lesson. Read through Resource Sheet 7 and place the items on the likelihood scale before allowing the children to move on to Resource Sheet 8.

■ Challenge

Ask the children to create statements of their own and place these on a likelihood scale.

PLENARY

Use the display likelihood scale to record the ideas of each group concerning the statements on Resource Sheet 8. Deal with differences of view, as appropriate, as you progress through the statements.

> **Key fact or strategy**
> Judging the likelihood of an event is a key skill in everyday life. It is on the basis of probabilities that we commonly make decisions.

Lesson 4

✎ Learning objectives

Mental/oral starter:
- Recall addition and subtraction facts for each number up to 20

Main teaching activities:
- Discuss chance or likelihood
- Present and interpret data on bar charts or bar line graphs
- Recognise when intermediate points have no meaning

📖 Resources

Two sets of cards numbered 1–20, Resource Sheet 9, General Resource Sheet A (You will need to make pattern spinners and number spinners before the lesson.), an OHT of Resource Sheet 9

ᵃᵇᶜ Vocabulary

Addition, subtraction, likelihood, chance, bar chart, bar line, graph, frequency

MENTAL/ORAL STARTER

Deal out the cards until all the children have one each. Choose pairs of children randomly to show the card that they have and say the number on it. Ask the class to tell you the sum and the difference for each pair. Continue for most or all pairs in the class.

MAIN ACTIVITY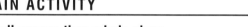

Small groups then whole class

Group the children so that there are six groups and give three of these patterned spinners and the other three the numbered spinners.

Tell the children:
We are going to make some charts and to do this we need some information.

Each group must spin the spinner that they have twenty-four times. Each time they record the result. (Remind the children about tallying as this may be a good way to keep a record.)

When the children are ready, display the OHT of Resource Sheet 9. Ask each of the three groups that used the patterned spinners to combine their results. (It may be useful to draw patterns in columns on the board for this.) When the results are aggregated, ask the children how you could use these to draw a bar chart on the OHT. When you have done this and you feel that the children understand, wipe off the bar chart and replace it with a bar line graph. Repeat the process with the groups who used the numbered spinners.

■ Support

Go over the instructions again and show how to tally, as necessary.

■ Challenge

Ask the children to think of examples where the highest points of each bar line can be joined.

PLENARY

Use the two bar line graphs. Ask:
Are these graphs/charts what you expected?

Discuss what the children say about this. Theoretically each line should be the same height but experimentally there are usually variations.

Why might we have results that we didn't expect?

If we did more spins what might happen?

Can I join the tops of the lines together?

In both cases this cannot be done. The patterned example should be readily understood but confusion can arise when numbers are used.

Why can't we join the tops?

Ask the children to write down the totals for each experiment and draw the charts for homework.

Key fact or strategy

In some cases it is not appropriate to join points (like those at the tops of bar lines to make line graphs).

Lesson 5

✎ Learning objectives
Mental/oral starter:
- Double or halve any whole number up to 100

Main teaching activities:
- Present and interpret data on bar charts or bar line graphs
- Recognise when intermediate points have no meaning

📖 Resources
Calculators, photocopies of Resource Sheets 10, 11, and 12, an OHT of the graph on Resource Sheet 10 (or the whole resource sheet if you can magnify this sufficiently when displayed)

🔤 Vocabulary
Double, halve, bar line, bar chart, points

MENTAL/ORAL STARTER

Give out calculators, at least one between two, if possible. Ask each pair to think of a number greater than 1 and less than 50 and enter it in the calculator. They write the number down with its double and use the calculator to check this. Ask different pairs to offer their chosen number and ask the class to mentally calculate its double. The pair should check that they are given the correct answer. Next, ask for the half of a number but use even numbers only.

MAIN ACTIVITY

Whole class, pairs

Give out Resource Sheet 10 and also display it on the OHP. Read through the introduction to the sheet.

What do we have to do?

Put the points and bar lines on the graph with the help of the children. Now ask the children to help each other to do their own copy. When they have done this, ask pairs to work out the answers to the questions. Ask the class for answers when these are available. Discuss the answers as appropriate.

Can we join the tops of the lines?

They cannot be joined because each line represents the number of days. There is no missing data and there are no points between.

Give out Resource Sheet 11. Ask pairs to read it carefully and then work through the questions.

■ Support
Give the children another opportunity to tackle Resource Sheet 10. Keep reinforcing the fact that we should not join points unless there can be a value between the points.

■ Challenge
Give Resource Sheet 12 to those who have progressed quickly.

PLENARY

Collect answers from different pairs of children from their work on Resource Sheet 11. Use this opportunity to review what a bar line means and how we know its length.

Can we join the tops of the lines?

Resource Sheet 12 can be given as homework.

Key fact or strategy
There are no intermediate points on these bar line graphs.

11

Lesson 6

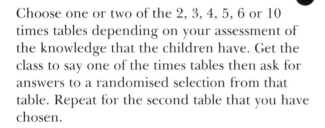

Learning objectives

Mental/oral starter:
- Recall facts in times tables

Main teaching activities:
- Present and interpret data on bar charts or bar line graphs
- Recognise when intermediate points have no meaning

Resources

The OHT of Resource Sheet 10 from the previous lesson, photocopies of Resource Sheet 13, make an OHT of a completed graph on Resource Sheet 13, photocopies of Resource Sheet 14 and General Resource Sheet B

Vocabulary

Bar line, bar chart, points

MENTAL/ORAL STARTER

Choose one or two of the 2, 3, 4, 5, 6 or 10 times tables depending on your assessment of the knowledge that the children have. Get the class to say one of the times tables then ask for answers to a randomised selection from that table. Repeat for the second table that you have chosen.

MAIN ACTIVITY

Whole class, pairs

Use the OHT of Resource Sheet 10 to remind the children how to draw a bar line graph and the way in which we mark and label the axes. Give out Resource Sheet 13. Ask pairs to work together to help each other draw a graph. When they have done this, invite different pairs to show their graphs to the class. Show the one on the OHT.

Does anyone want to change their graph?

Ask the children to think of four questions that they could pose about the topic. Invite selected pairs to ask one of their questions to the class and encourage other children to answer.

Draw axes on the board to help with making the chart for Resource Sheet 14. Give out the resource sheet and General Resource Sheet B for the chart. The children continue to work in pairs.

■ **Support**

Give the children help with making the first chart. Talk through ideas for possible questions.

■ **Challenge**

The children can develop additional questions.

PLENARY

Ask different pairs to share their charts with other pairs. Complete the chart that you have started on the board.

What was easy about this chart?

What was difficult?

Can we join the points on either of these charts?

Collect in the charts to help evaluate the children's progress and understanding.

Key fact or strategy

To draw bar line graphs we need to mark the axes appropriately in 2s, 5s, 10s, 100s, and so on, depending on the size of the frequencies.

Learning objectives

Mental/oral starter:
- Recall multiplication facts

Main teaching activity:
- Make a simple database on paper

Resources

Tables tests in two tables (for example, 6s and 8s), photocopies of Resource Sheet 15, two sets of test results from the past that you have in your record books (These can be reproduced on an OHT or a sheet that you photocopy and can be modified in order to help with the data organisation. You might also sample and/or change names.)

Vocabulary

Data, database, mode, maximum, minimum, range

MENTAL/ORAL STARTER

Invite the class to tell you the 6 and the 8 times tables. Give short tests on each of these. The tests should include questions such as:

What are five 8s?

If the product is 48 what is the multiplication in the 6 times table?

Collect in the tests for marking. The results can be utilised in data lessons next year.

MAIN ACTIVITY

Whole class, pairs

Use the test results that you have assembled. Ask the children to show how the data can be organised by putting the scores in order from highest to lowest for each test. Point out that there is a score from the first test that most people seemed to get.

What is that score?

The same applies to the second test.

What is that score?

Explain that this is a sort of average that we call the *mode*. Write this term on the board.

Who got the mode on test one? ... test two?

Give out Resource Sheet 15. Tell the children that you have been given some scores out of ten that pet owners gave for how much they think that their cat likes the food. The full list is shown here.

Cat food preferences

The full set of marks out of ten is:

	Cattodins	Pussygrub
Alan	9	6
Bryony	8	8
Corinne	8	9
Darren	10	8
Iqbal	10	7
Fiona	9	8
Sumi	7	8
Heather	9	7
Isobel	9	5
Jack	8	10

Read out the scores. You can do this in any order. The children should work in pairs to complete the table on the resource sheet. When they have done this tell them to answer the first two questions on the sheet. Get answers to these.

Is the manufacturer of Cattodins correct?

Point out that these ten children agree, but we cannot really say that it is true for everyone. The manufacturer ought really to state that most of the people they have asked prefer to give their cats Cattodins.

Now tell the children that there are other things that we can look at in these data. With their help, organise the scores for both pet foods from highest to lowest.

What is the highest/lowest for each?

Now explain that the difference between the highest and the lowest is called the *range*. Write this term on the board.

What are the ranges here?

Ask the children to complete questions 2 and 4 on the sheet.

■ Support

Make one or two copies of Resource Sheet 15 with all the figures entered correctly. Give these to the children who have difficulty in transposing the information.

■ Challenge

From the attendance records, the children could study the numbers at school each week for three or four weeks and answer the questions: What is the mode? What is the range?

Look back at the data from the times table test. Ask the children to work out the range for each. Use this opportunity to reinforce the meaning of *mode*. Tell the children that what they have worked on are two sets of data. When we have a collection of data we sometimes call this a *database*. Write this one the board.

Key fact or strategy

The mode is a sort of average that means the most common score or item in a set.

Lesson 8

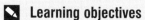

✎ Learning objectives

Mental/oral starter:
• Multiply or divide whole numbers to 10 000 by 10 or 100
Main teaching activity:
• Make a simple database on paper

📖 Resources

Calculators, a mixed set of story books and/or text books

🔤 Vocabulary

Data, database, mode, average, range

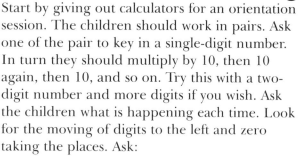

MENTAL/ORAL STARTER

Start by giving out calculators for an orientation session. The children should work in pairs. Ask one of the pair to key in a single-digit number. In turn they should multiply by 10, then 10 again, then 10, and so on. Try this with a two-digit number and more digits if you wish. Ask the children what is happening each time. Look for the moving of digits to the left and zero taking the places. Ask:

If I multiply a number by 10 and by 10 again, what is the same as ... multiplying by?

Finish by thinking of whole numbers and ask individuals to mentally calculate the effect of multiplying by 10 or by 100.

MAIN ACTIVITY

Whole class, pairs or small groups

Tell the children that in this lesson they are going to do some research on the alphabet. Give out different books to pairs of children. Work through the steps that you want them to take. These are:

1 Open at any page.
2 Look at the first three lines of print.
3 Make a tally of all of the letters used in the three lines.
4 Total the numbers of times letters are used.

When the children are ready, ask different pairs:

What would you say is the most common letter?

Which are the uncommon letters?

Record the results from the whole class and combine them to see what seems to be the most used letter in the alphabet. Can the children say anything about this letter (and other common letters)? What about the least used ones? Remind the children that the most common letter is the mode when we are using English, it might be different in other languages. What is the range?

■ **Support**

Remind the children how to organise a table for tallying.

■ **Challenge**

Some children can work on counting syllables to see whether there are differences according to the subject of text books and/or the age range of the books. (This is the basis of much work on "readability".)

PLENARY

Use the work done in this and the last lesson to review what *mode* and *range* mean.

Key fact or strategy

To do data work it is necessary to be thoughtful about how to organise the data collection. Tallying is a useful approach.

Supplementary activities

Mental/oral follow-up

Much of the work done in these lessons has been about multiplication and the associated division facts. Create a multiplication table display area and use any available short-time periods to rehearse one or more of the tables. Let the children "play" with inputting numbers to the calculator then experimenting with multiplication and division. What do they discover? Let the children who observe exciting outcomes explain these to others.

Homework

The games involving dice outlined under "Development" could be played at home. Make photocopies of likelihood scales and get the children to create some statements that can be placed on the scale. Provide some data (or get the children to collect some) and ask the children to draw bar charts and/or bar line graphs. Examples could include colours of cars passing the school in a given time, or the colour of front doors in the street.

Development

Make as much use as possible of games of chance and games involving both chance and skill. Encourage the children to talk about these. Stimulate discussion about "fair" and "not fair". To promote such discussion it is worth setting up games, for example, tell the children that, in pairs, they are going to play a game by using dice. They have to play the game and then decide whether it is fair for both players. They will need to keep a tally of their scores and the first one to get to 25 points will win. Give out dice and tell the children which person in each pair is Player 1 and which is Player 2. On each go, the player rolls both dice and totals them. If Player 1 rolls a total of 2, 3, 4, 10, 11 or 12, then they get a point. If the total is 5, 6, 7, 8 or 9, then Player 2 gets the point. Player 2 then rolls and totals in the same way and the same rules apply. Write the totals that apply to each player on the board. Remind them that the first one to get to 25 points wins. Ask whether Player 1 or 2 won in each case. The children should find that Player 2 is the usual winner. Ask why this might be so. How many chances does Player 2 have to gain a point? How many chances does Player 1 have? Can they think of ways of making the game fairer?

Play a track game where one player doesn't roll at all but always moves on 4 spaces when it's their turn. The other player rolls a dice and moves on the amount shown on the dice for their turn. The person getting to the end of the track first wins. Organise the children to play this game. Discuss any surprising outcomes.

ICT ideas

Granada Database (part of the Granada toolkit) is a fully featured data-handling package, where children can collect and store information. The package includes a range of graphing facilities including bar charts and bar line graphs. Database packages such as this should be used in a whole-class setting during mathematics lessons, as much time can be wasted in familiarising children with the creation of the database structure. With the data collected from the children's "paper databases", a central database could be established for everyone to use.

Unit 3 Measures problems, including time

Term

Autumn 8–10

Framework links

8–10	15	102–111	Shape and space	Identify and recognise properties of rectangles. Classify triangles: isosceles, equilateral, scalene; lines of symmetry. Recognise positions, read and plot co-ordinates in the first quadrant.
		76–81	Reasoning about shapes	Solve shape puzzles. Explain methods and reasoning orally and in writing.
		86–101	Measures, including problems	Understand, measure and calculate perimeter of rectangles, regular polygons. Measure and draw lines to the nearest mm. Use, read and write standard metric units of length, abbreviations and relationships. Convert larger to smaller units of length. Know mile. Read the time on 24-hour digital clock, for example, 19:53. Suggest suitable units/equipment to estimate or measure length. Record estimates/measurements from scales to suitable degree of accuracy. Use all four operations to solve measurement word problems, including time. Choose appropriate operations/calculation methods. Explain working.

Setting the scene

The work in this school year builds on that which the children did in Year 4/P5. They are given the opportunity to use the skills and knowledge they have already acquired and solve problems that may be a little more complex. The unit has two main themes. Firstly, we engage the children with work on length. They carry out an investigation about length and are given word problems to tackle. The second half of the unit is devoted to work on time. Two different contexts are offered so that a full range of time challenges is available.

Starting points

The children know the major units of measurement of length, both metric and imperial. They have worked on hours and minutes. In this unit they can employ their knowledge of seconds.

Checking progress

- All children should be able to indicate that they know the relationships between common units of measurement of length. They should be able to identify which operations are necessary and attempt to solve word problems involving measures of length. They should be able to try to solve problems involving time, and describe their approaches.
- Children requiring additional support will need to be reminded of the relationships between common units of measurement of length. They need support in remembering how measures of time are associated with one another and how we denote time.
- Some children will have progressed further. They can describe and explain their approaches in solving word problems involving measures of length and time.

Lesson 1

 Learning objectives
Mental/oral starter:
- Convert metres to centimetres
- Convert centimetres to metres

Main teaching activities:
- Use addition, subtraction, multiplication and division to solve word problems involving measures of length

Resources
A metre stick marked up in centimetres, a 30 cm rule marked in millimetres, enough centimetre rules for each child to have one, paper samples of A3 and A5 sizes, photocopies of Resource Sheet 16

Vocabulary
Centimetres, metres

MENTAL/ORAL STARTER

Write the headings for a two-column chart on the board as shown here.

Metres	Centimetres
	250
7.6	
16.02	
	13 000
4	
17.1	
	75
	140
	0.2

Enter numbers on the chart, one at a time, and ask the children to convert them. Invite individual children to add numbers to the chart so that their classmates can say what they are in metres or centimetres.

MAIN ACTIVITY

Whole class, individuals

Show the metre stick marked up in centimetres and a 30 cm rule marked in millimetres. Ask the children about the units depicted on these measuring instruments. Remind the children of the importance of placing a centimetre rule so that the scale begins at the beginning of the line or object being measured.

Give each child a centimetre rule. Talk about the association between millimetres and centimetres. Allow the children to measure their pencils, and across their paper or their exercise book in centimetres and millimetres.

Give each child a copy of Resource Sheet 16 and read it through to the class. Allow the children time to work on it individually.

■ Support
Invite the children to try measuring, as exactly as they can, the A4 resource sheet, and sheets of paper that are A3 and A5. They can look at the pattern of measurements and use a calculator to fill in the gaps in the chart on the resource sheet to see how accurate their measurements have been.

■ Challenge
Ask the children to work out the sizes of A6 and A7 paper. Can they spot papers of all the "A" sizes in use in the classroom?

PLENARY

Show all the class the sample pieces of paper of A3 and A5 size. Discuss with them what all the paper sizes in their charts would be in centimetres.

> **Key fact or strategy**
> "A" sizes in paper have a logical explanation.

Lesson 2

◣ Learning objectives

Mental/oral starter:
- Double whole numbers to 100

Main teaching activities:
- Use addition, subtraction, multiplication and division to solve word problems involving measures of length
- Explain how they worked them out

📖 Resources

Two blank dice, one of which should be marked up 0, 1, 2, 3, 4, 5 and the other 0, 5, 6, 7, 8 and 9, enough metre sticks for one between two children, photocopies of Resource Sheet 17

abc Vocabulary

Digit, double, kilometre, metre

MENTAL/ORAL STARTER

Throw the 0–5 dice twice, to give two digits. Call out these digits, firstly in one order and then the other. Invite the children to say what double this number is, for example, if 2 and 5 are thrown, call out 25 and then 52. The children respond with 50 and 104. Throw the pairs of dice several times to give different numbers. Then throw the 0–5 dice and the 0, 5, 6, 7, 8, 9 dice together. Make 2 two-digit numbers from the numbers thrown. The children should double these numbers. Finally, have several goes at throwing the 0–9 dice twice. Make 2 two-digit numbers from the numbers thrown. The children can double these.

MAIN ACTIVITY

Whole class, pairs, whole class, individuals

Give each pair of children a metre stick. Talk about some of the things we might measure in metres. By using their metre stick to visualise their estimates, the children can estimate the length or height of two or three objects within sight of the classroom. These objects can be written on the board. They could, for example, include a carpet, a wall, a bush, and a netball post. Discuss the children's estimates and why they think a metre is a suitable unit to use to measure them.

Show the children how to read a distance chart like the one on the Resource Sheet 17. Give each child a copy of the resource sheet. Invite them to try to solve the problems.

▪ Support

Ask the children to read aloud all the distances from one city to another from the chart at the top of the resource sheet. Return to help them discuss Bob and his fences when they are ready.

▪ Challenge

Tell the children that Bob has managed to get hold of 2 metre fencing panels to add to his stock.

How does this help him find other ways to make up fences of the given lengths?

PLENARY

Invite pairs of children to tell the class of the method they used in solving one of the challenges on the resource sheet. Discuss alternative methods.

Key fact or strategy

We measure long distances in kilometres. Metres are an everyday measure of length of objects such as walls and fences.

Lesson 3

⬚ Learning objectives
Mental/oral starter:
- Double multiples of 10 up to 1 000

Main teaching activities:
- Use addition, subtraction, multiplication and division to solve word problems involving time

📖 Resources
Before the lesson, in a long line on a strip of paper or on a long board, write up the multiples of 10 to 1 000, as follows, 10, 20, 30, 40, 50, 60, 70, 80, 90, 100, 110, 120, 130, 140, 150, 160, 170, 180, 190, 200, 210, and so on. A large class-sized cardboard clock, photocopies of Resource Sheet 18

ᵃᵇᶜ Vocabulary
Hour, minute, second

MENTAL/ORAL STARTER

Tell the children that they are going to practise doubling multiples of 10 up to 1 000. Use the line of multiples of 10 and point to 10, 20, 30, and so on. Ask the children to double each number. Then point to numbers at random and ask for the double. Give volunteer children the opportunity to come to the front of the class and point out numbers of which other children can call out the double.

MAIN ACTIVITY

Whole class, individuals

Use the class-sized clock face to confirm that all the children are confident about the concepts of hour, minute and second, and how they are related. Write some times in longhand on the board. Here are some examples.

Twenty to twelve	Quarter past four
9 p.m.	
Seventeen minutes past eight	
Twelve midnight	

Talk through with the children how time is denoted and how times using a 24-hour clock are written.

Give a copy of Resource Sheet 18 to each child and ask everyone to see how quickly they can complete the challenges by writing their workings into their work books or on rough paper and the answers in the boxes on the Resource Sheet.

■ Support
Work with the children to spell out, for each calculation, the answers to the following:

1 What kind of calculation should I do to solve this puzzle?
2 What operations are involved?
3 Am I working with hours, minutes, seconds?
4 What is the correct way to write the answer?

■ Challenge
Ask the children to work in pairs to confirm and check the answers and to compare methods.

PLENARY

Take one sample calculation from Resource Sheet 18, say, number 3, about the kiddy ride. Modify it to construct a new set of calculations, for example, if rides were twelve minutes, one minute or three minutes long, what would the finish times be? This gives more opportunities to discuss methods that may be used to reach a solution. If there is time, choose another challenge from the resource sheet and modify that.

Key fact or strategy
Understanding time requires knowledge of the 24-hour clock and the association between second, minute and hour.

Lesson 4

◤ Learning objectives
Mental/oral starter:
- Multiply whole numbers up to 10000 by 10

Main teaching activities:
- Use addition, subtraction, multiplication and division to solve word problems involving time
- Explain how they worked them out

◧ Resources
A large class-sized cardboard clock, photocopies of Resource Sheet 19, a music CD (Choose one that will be popular with the children and has the playing time for each track on it.)

ᵃᵦᶜ Vocabulary
Hour, minute, second

MENTAL/ORAL STARTER

Write on the board a row of 4 digits. They can be any combination, for example, 5098. Make lists of the two-, three- and four-digit numbers that can be made from these digits, as shown.

5098

50	509	5099
59	508	5980
58	598	5089
98	590	etc.
85	580	
80	589	
89	980	
90	985	
95	950	
	908	
	905	
	850	
	809	
	805	
	890	
	895	
	etc.	

Go down each list and invite the children to multiply each number by ten. The two-digit numbers may go 50, 500; 59, 590; 58, 580. The children should quickly be able to determine what happens to the place value of the digits when a number is multiplied by ten.

MAIN ACTIVITY

Whole class, individuals, pairs

On the board, create a doctor's appointment timing list. Make appointments 10, 7, 5, 3, 12, 20 and 15 minutes long. Here is a suggested list for the beginning of morning surgery.

8:30	8:45	9:32
8:37	8:57	
8:42	9:17	

Discuss the time taken for each appointment and for the appointments in total. Point out that the list is a *timetable*.

Invite the children to each take a copy of Resource Sheet 19 and try to solve the time puzzles apart from the "Ultimate challenge".

■ Support
Read the whole resource sheet with the children. Discuss the concepts of minutes and seconds and then begin the first challenge. Re-visit the group several times during the session to check progress.

■ Challenge
The children find a partner. They work out the "Ultimate challenge" together.

PLENARY

Take up the CD and ask the children to solve challenges related to the timing of each track.

Key fact or strategy
Understanding time requires knowledge of how we write minutes and seconds.

Supplementary activities

Mental/oral follow-up   Ask the children to convert lists of measures in metres into centimetres, and vice versa.

Homework   Ask the children to find a music CD or TV programme listings magazine and invent and solve four challenges associated with track playing times or the duration of programmes.

Development   Look for lists of timings and measures in other locations, for example, timetables and shopping catalogues. Use these to create and solve word problems involving measures of length.

Use the distance chart on Resource Sheet 17 or distance charts from road atlases to give the children the opportunity to convert kilometres to miles and vice versa.

For an approximation:
miles to km $\times$ 1.5
km to miles $\div$ 1.5

For an accurate answer:
miles to km $\times$ 1.609
km to miles $\div$ 0.621

ICT ideas   *Can Do Maths Year 5/P6 CD3* includes "A family outing", a multi-layered problem-solving activity based around the theme of a family journey to the seaside. There are five destinations on the journey. Each destination generates a problem to be solved involving all four operations. The activity is suitable for one child or pairs working co-operatively.

Unit 4 Money and "real-life" problems

Term				Autumn 11

Framework links

11	5	40–47	Mental calculation strategies (+ and –)	Find differences by counting up through next multiple of 10, 100, 1000. Partition into HTU and add most significant digits first.
		48–51	Pencil and paper procedures (+ and –)	Use informal pencil and paper methods. Extend written methods to +/– of two integers less than 10000.
		82–85	Money and "real-life" problems	Use all four operations to solve money and "real-life" word problems.
		70–75	Making decisions, checking results, including using a calculator	Choose appropriate operations/calculation methods. Explain working. Check calculations using inverse operation, including with calculator.

Setting the scene

The work here follows that of Unit 1 where the children practised solving money and "real-life" challenges, discussed the methods they used and worked on estimating as a way of checking. Money is something that the children are familiar with in everyday life so it is appropriate to create realistic contexts for exploration in the classroom. In this unit we are using summer in the garden, toys, and pocket/holiday money.

Starting points

The children have already had the opportunity to solve one-step and multi-step money and "real-life" problems, involving all four operations. They have also practised estimating their answers. This unit offers opportunities for them to practise checking by using inverse operations.

Checking progress

- All children can use addition, subtraction, multiplication and division to solve money problems. Because they should also be able to check their calculations using inverse operations, problems have been made single-step.
- Children requiring additional support will need to be confident about the operation they are to use, before tackling the arithmetic. They would benefit from whole-class work on the idea of inverse operations.
- Some children will have progressed further and be able to create greater challenges for themselves.

Lesson 1

◥ Learning objectives

Mental/oral starter:
- Convert pounds to pence
- Convert pence to pounds

Main teaching activities:
- Use addition, subtraction, multiplication and division to solve money problems
- Check calculations using inverse operations

▨ Resources

Make a number of large price tags, placed in two sets, A and B. Print on one side of each a price in pounds and pence, and on the other a price in pence. Here are suggested sets of prices for Set A and Set B.

£4.62

front of card

Set A

£4.62	462p	£3.36	336p	£1.02	102p
£156.32	15 632p	£0.17	17p	£76.84	7 684p
£100.06	10 006p	£326	32 600p	£7.10	710p

462p

back of card

Set B

£14.36	1 436p	£1 056.73	105 673	£0.56	56p
102p	£1.02	£777.77	77 777p	1 616p	£16.16
£50.01	5 001p	£35.53	3 553p	1 011p	£10.11
£52	5 200p	£11.61	1 161p	17p	£0.17

Photocopies of Resource Sheet 20

Vocabulary

Pound, pence

MENTAL/ORAL STARTER 🕙

Hold up each of the price labels in Set A in turn and ask a child to convert the price to pounds and pence, or to pence according to which side is shown.

Place the class in four groups and hold each of the prices in Set B up in turn. Ask one member of each group in turn for an answer. The first to answer correctly takes the card for their group, and the next question is aimed at the next group around the room. The winning group has most cards.

MAIN ACTIVITY 🕥

Whole class, individuals, pairs

Practise adding two of the prices used in the mental/oral starter, so that the children are reminded of what happens when the number of

pence exceeds 100. Try out several of these prices by doing subtraction, multiplication and division.

Give the children a copy of Resource Sheet 20. Invite them to solve the challenges.

■ Support

Take the children through the operation they will use for each challenge in turn.

■ Challenge

Ask the children to work with a partner to create three more problems by using the "Summer garden fun" prices set out on the resource sheet.

PLENARY

Work through the challenges on Resource Sheet 20 with the children. Take each in turn and discuss the appropriate methods to use. When an answer is obtained show how reverse operations can be used to check the answer. Here is the first challenge, *What was the original price of the barbecue?*, worked through, with some of the key questions.

How can we work out this price?

What kind of operation do we need to do? (addition)

What are the ways we could use to add the current price and the "money off" together?

Approximate by adding £25 and £5 and taking away 1p; add £24 and £5 and then add the 99p.

To check the answer of £29.99, we can say what is £29.99 minus the "money off" of £5? This is using subtraction, the reverse of the original addition.

Key fact or strategy
We can use reverse operations to check answers.

Lesson 2

Learning objectives
Mental/oral starter:
• Multiply whole numbers up to 10 000 by 100
Main teaching activities:
• Use addition, subtraction, multiplication and division to solve money problems
• Check calculations using inverse operations

Resources
Write each of the digits 0–9 on sticky labels or on pieces of card, photocopies of Resource Sheets 21 and 22

Vocabulary
Digit, problem

MENTAL/ORAL STARTER

Lay all the digit cards out face up on the front desk. Allow a number of children in turn to come out and by using the digit cards, stick onto the board any four-digit number. When a fresh number appears the children are asked firstly what is that number multiplied by 10 and then what is that number multiplied by 100?

MAIN ACTIVITY

Whole class, small groups

Explain to the children that they are to solve some word problems. Remind them of the need to sort out the kind of operation to be used. Give each small group a number of copies of Resource Sheet 21 and invite them to work together to solve the problems and make a note of differences in the methods chosen by different members of the group.

■ **Support**
Work together with the children to solve the first of the problems. Ask them to try the next amongst themselves. Re-visit them to check that

they are solving the problems with confidence.

■ **Challenge**
Give groups who finish a large sheet of paper on which, as a group, they should complete a large drawing of the "Quickie Meal" burger house, along with their own data about how many seats, counter staff and a complete menu with prices. They can then, if there is time, create challenges related to this data. This is a draft attempt at the development task, set out in detail on page 26.

PLENARY

Call the class together and work systematically through the resource sheet challenges, one at a time. In each case the children should have the opportunity to discuss their methods and a check should be made of each answer by using an inverse calculation.

Key fact or strategy
Inverse operations can be used as a check.

Supplementary activities

Mental/oral follow-up

Take the digits 0–9, on separate pieces of card, as in Lesson 2. Use each digit once or twice to create several four-digit numbers. Ask the children the following questions about each number.

What is this number multiplied by 100?

If this number were pence, how many pounds would I have?

If this number were pounds, how many pence would I have?

If the number is 1831, the answers to the questions will be 183100, read as one hundred and eighty-three thousand, one hundred; £18.31 and 183100 pence.

Homework

Resource Sheet 22 provides the children with opportunities to work on some pocket money problems. They can take this home and then return the work to school for further discussion.

Development

Take up the idea raised in Lesson 2 and invite the children to create their own "Quickie Meal" burger house by doing a large illustration, along with their own data about how many seats, counter staff and a complete menu with prices. They can then create a set of "real-life" and money problems attached to their own burger house. If these are word-processed or written up on resource sheets they can be photocopied and tackled by the whole class.

ICT ideas

Lifeskills Time and Money (Learning and Teaching Scotland) offers a range of stimulating activities set within a townscape where children are encouraged to learn by solving puzzles and managing everyday situations. The teacher can customise the content of this package to meet the needs of individual ability levels.

Unit 5 Money and "real-life" problems

Term Spring 2–3

Framework links

2-3	10	52–57	Understanding × and ÷	Begin to use brackets. Use factors.
		60–65	Mental calculation strategies (× and ÷)	Use closely related facts (derive ×19 from ×20, ×12 from ×10 add ×2). Partition, for example, 47 × 6.
		66–69	Pencil and paper procedures (× and ÷)	Extend written methods to HTU ÷ U (whole number remainder).
		82–85	Money and "real-life" problems	Use all four operations to solve money or "real-life" word problems.
		70–75	Making decisions and checking results including using a calculator	Choose appropriate operations/calculation methods. Explain working. Check with inverse operation or equivalent calculation.

Setting the scene

The children will have completed two units involving money and "real-life" problems during the autumn term. Their work included practice at estimating and using inverse operations to check answers. In this unit, the work makes use of number operations and links division with fractions. Again, as with all the units that are concerned with "real life", we are providing contexts that connect with the everyday experiences of children. The themes and topics include, for example, coins and stamps, school materials, and a garden centre.

Starting points

The work builds on the prodigious skills that the children have in solving problems. In this unit the first lesson focuses on reasoning problems that involve coins and postage stamps. The second and third lessons include work on "real-life" problems and all four operations.

Checking progress

- All the children should be able to say what kinds of operations are required to solve problems and how they worked out the answers.
- Children requiring additional support will be able to work through some of the problems once they have discussed the steps they need to take to reach an answer.
- Some children will have progressed further. They will be able to complete the challenges with ease and go on to create more of their own.

Lesson 1

Learning objectives

Mental/oral starter:
- Identify pairs of numbers that sum to 100

Main teaching activities:
- Use addition, subtraction, multiplication and division to solve money problems
- Explain how the problems were solved

Resources

Make an OHT of Resource Sheet 23 (if required for the mental/oral starter), photocopies of Resource Sheet 24

Vocabulary

Fewest, coins, amount

MENTAL/ORAL STARTER

Set up Resource Sheet 23 on the overhead projector or write up on the board the first column of numbers that appear on this resource sheet. By working with the overhead transparency, you can point to any number at random and ask an individual child to identify the pair number that sums to 100. Thus, if you point to 42 the child should say 58 as 42 + 58 sum to 100. With a water-soluble OHT pen, you can draw a line to join 42 and 58.

If working on the board, with the children's help, write alongside the column of numbers, the pair numbers that sum to 100. The children will quickly be able to detect the pattern. When they have worked on two or three columns of numbers in order, write up numbers at random, and ask individual children to name the pair number that will bond to 100.

MAIN ACTIVITY

Whole class, individuals, pairs

Write 30p on the board.

Say to the children:

I want you to think about the coins that you could use to make 30p. For example, we could make 30p by using three 10p coins. What are the other ways we could make 30p?

The children's answers should include:

1 × 20p, 1 × 10p
1 × 20p, 2 × 5p
1 × 20p, 1 × 5p, 2 × 2p, 1 × 1p
1 × 20p, 1 × 5p, 1 × 2p, 3 × 1p
1 × 20p, 1 × 5p, 5 × 1p
1 × 20p, 10 × 1p
2 × 10p, 2 × 5p

2 × 10p, 1 × 5p, 2 × 2p, 1 × 1p
2 × 10p, 1 × 5p, 1 × 2p, 3 × 1p
2 × 10p, 1 × 5p, 5 × 1p
2 × 10p, 10 × 1p
6 × 5p
5 × 5p, 2 × 2p, 1 × 1p
5 × 5p, 1 × 2p, 3 × 1p

Hand out copies of Resource Sheet 24, and give the children time to tackle each of the puzzles, writing their answers into their workbooks.

■ Support
Ask the children to work in pairs on just the first challenge on the resource sheet.

■ Challenge
Children who work speedily through the challenges should work with a partner to list, for each challenge, the operations they used, and discuss their working out.

(The children may take longer than the time allowed in the lesson to complete them. They can be given finishing time in another session or as a homework activity.)

PLENARY

Work through the first challenge on Resource Sheet 24 with the whole class. Discuss methods, approaches, and ways of setting down the answers in a systematic way.

> **Key fact or strategy**
> Think clearly and logically. Set down workings out systematically.

Lesson 2

◣ Learning objectives
Mental/oral starter:
- Multiples of fifty that sum to 1 000

Main teaching activities:
- Use addition, subtraction, multiplication and division to solve "real-life" problems
- Explain how the problems were solved

■ Resources
Make an OHT or photocopy of Resource Sheet 25 (if required for the mental/oral starter), a box containing 35 pencils, photocopies of Resource Sheet 26

Vocabulary
Multiple, number bond, operation, add, subtract, multiply, divide, invent, challenge

MENTAL/ORAL STARTER

Show the OHT of Resource Sheet 25 but mask both columns of figures. Invite the children to give you multiples of 50, starting 50, 100, 150, and so on. Reveal the products in the left-hand list as the children call them out. Then reveal the numbers in the right-hand list, beginning at the bottom and working up the list.

Return to the top of the left-hand list and again mask the right-hand set of numbers. Ask the children:
What multiple of 50 do we need to add to 50 to make 1 000?

Again, as the children respond with the bond number, reveal that number in the right-hand list. Finally cover the left-hand numbers and identify the matching bonds to a 1 000 for each right-hand number.

If you choose not to use the overhead projector, write the numbers on a white board. Mask both lists to start with, in exactly the way described above.

MAIN ACTIVITY

Whole class, pairs

Show the children the box of 35 pencils and create some story problems to go with these. Here are some suggestions.

There are thirty-five pencils in this box. How many would I have in nine such boxes?

If Sam and Madge share three boxes of pencils with three friends, how many pencils will they have each?

New supplies include five boxes and three boxes. How many new pencils is that?

Of the 350 pencils in the cupboard at the beginning of term, 128 have been taken for use. How many are left?

Give each pair of children a copy of Resource Sheet 26. Ask them to try out the story problems there.

■ Support
Support the pairs of children by setting up the first challenge with them. Talk through the operation to use and how to go about it. Return to help them with the next challenge, if necessary.

■ Challenge
Give these children a new item for the school stock cupboard. It could, for example, be 47 rolls of sticky tape or 550 gold stars. Ask them to create several story problems related to this new item.

PLENARY

Choose some of the problems created by the pairs of children who were able to invent more challenges. Solve these as a class.

Key fact or strategy
Think clearly and logically. Set down workings out systematically.

Lesson 3

▶ Learning objectives
Mental/oral starter:
- Memorise or compute quickly decimals that sum to one
- Memorise or compute quickly decimals that sum to ten

Main teaching activities:
- Use addition, subtraction, multiplication and division to solve "real-life" problems
- Explain how the problems were solved
- Check answers using an inverse operation or equivalent calculation

📖 Resources
Photocopies of Resource Sheet 27, a garden centre catalogue

Vocabulary
Number bond, operation, decimal, add, subtract, multiply, divide

MENTAL/ORAL STARTER

Set the scene for the activity by asking the children to give you examples of number bonds to ten. When the children have called out all the number pairs, ask:

Now what are the pairs of numbers that we can use to make one?

They should respond with 0.5 and 0.5, 0.2 and 0.8, and so on.

Finally look together at number bonds that involve decimals and make ten. The children should have a mental pattern that includes the following sequences.

0.25 and 0.75 make 1   2.5 and 7.5 make 10

MAIN ACTIVITY

Whole class, individuals, small groups

Write the following story problem up on the board:

At the garden centre Basil plants 15 seedlings in each row. How many are there in 8 rows? ... 18 rows?

If 279 grow strongly enough for potting on, and one third of these sell in the first week, how many are there left for sale?

Give out copies of Resource Sheet 27. Ask the children to work out the problems in their workbooks or on rough paper and enter the answers on the Resource Sheet.

▪ Support
Ask the children to tackle every problem and get as far as they can with it, asking themselves: What kinds of operations do I need? What is the order to do them in? If they cannot reach an answer they should consult you, or one of a number of specially chosen children, to get a clue to tackling the problem.

▪ Challenge
Ask the children to join with others into a group, investigate the garden centre catalogue, and make up challenges of their own involving all four operations.

PLENARY

Work through some or all of the problems on Resource Sheet 27. Discuss with the children the methods they use.

Key fact or strategy
In multi-step problem solving it is important to work one step at a time, and in the appropriate order.

Supplementary activities

Mental/oral follow-up

Generate target numbers with the help of the children. These numbers then have to be made by summing other numbers so, for example, if 10 is the target number then 7 + 3 or 8 + 2 would satisfy the requirement, if it is summing two numbers. However, you can vary the rules and ask for three numbers to be summed or four or whatever you choose. Making 10 might be 1 + 2 + 7 or 5 + 3 + 2, and so on. Include numbers less than 5 as targets so that decimals have to be used at times.

Homework

Collect some used stamps of a range of different values and stick them on pieces of card, in groups of three or four. The card pieces can then be laminated. Ask each child to take a card, and work out the different postage amounts they could make by using one or more of the stamps.

Development

Use the homework cards as a resource pool for the children to draw on in the future.

ICT ideas

Homepages.Maths.Year 5 (Nelson Thornes) includes a CD-ROM containing over 80 ready-made worksheets that build into a comprehensive homework package. As well as this, each book comes with a CD-ROM including editable versions of all the worksheets. By using this CD, the teacher can customise the worksheets (including many containing word problems) to meet the needs of individual children or use additional banks of prepared artwork for new contexts or consolidation work.

Unit 6 Measures problems

Term				Spring 7–8

Framework links

7–8	10	86–101	Measures including problems	Understand area measured in square centimetres. Use formula in words for area of rectangle. Use, read and write standard metric units of mass, abbreviations. Know relationships between them. Convert larger to smaller units of mass.
				Suggest suitable units and equipment to estimate or measure mass. Read measurements from scales. Use all four operations to solve measurement word problems. Choose appropriate operations/calculation methods. Explain working.
		112–117	Handling data	Represent and interpret data in a line graph (for example, weight of a baby at monthly intervals from birth to one year). Recognise when points can be joined to show trends.

Setting the scene

Measures and measuring are key features in our lives. So much of what we do involves measuring. We measure distances and lengths, weights of things, how much fuel for the car and our bank balances. Work on measures problems is both important and pertinent in the context of our everyday lives. Earlier in the year, in Unit 3, the children did some work on length and time. In this unit the ideas are all to do with mass. The demands are various but all include decisions about operations and methods of solving the word problems. Once again we have adopted a context which should have a connection with the lives of the children. This time it is food.

Starting points

The children have had copious experience in both problem-solving and measures units, in using standard measures. The work in this unit offers them opportunities to work on mass in "real-life" settings.

Checking progress

- All the children should be able to work out masses by using calculation.
- Children requiring additional support will need to be guided through an understanding of what is required.
- Some children will have progressed further and be able to modify the problems they have been given to create new challenges.

Lesson 1

◥ Learning objectives
Mental/oral starter:
- Round decimals with one decimal place to the nearest whole number

Main teaching activities:
- Use addition, subtraction, multiplication and division to solve measurement word problems, involving mass
- Explain how the problems were solved

◪ Resources
A book with several hundred pages to generate the numbers for the mental/oral starter, a kitchen balance marked in metric amounts, some items to weigh on the balance as a demonstration, photocopies of Resource Sheet 28

Vocabulary
Rounding, decimals, decimal point, digit, whole number, grams, weigh, weight, half, three-quarters

MENTAL/ORAL STARTER

Check that the children recall what is meant by rounding. Tell them that you would like them to round the decimals that you are going to call out, to the nearest whole number. Open the book at random and say the page number but place a decimal point before the final digit, for example, page 345 becomes 34.5 and 89 becomes 8.9. The children should say 35 and 9 in response. Continue to open the book at random to give the children a range of numbers to work on.

Invite a child to call out page numbers from the book, while another child points to individual children to supply the answer. Tease out the thinking behind some of the responses by asking:

Has the number been rounded up or down?

What do we mean by a whole number?

How do we know this answer is a whole number?

MAIN ACTIVITY

Whole class, individual

Weigh a few items on the kitchen balance. Call out the readings in grams. Check that the children know how many grams there are in a kilogram. Ask the children about the shopping and/or cooking that they do.

Do you ever make the supper?

Who likes pasta?

What makes a good topping for pasta?

Has anyone ideas about how much the ingredients for pasta dishes weigh?

Explain that you would like the children to try some problems related to pasta feast food. Give each child a copy of Resource Sheet 28 and see how they get on.

■ Support
Remind the children to tackle one step of a problem at a time and offer them key questions that give clues about what to do next, for example, in challenge 3 the questioning may go:
How much mushroom sauce is in the jar?
The problem says half is used. How do we find out half?
What do we find half of?
What is the answer?
It says the whole jar feeds 5 people.
How do we find out what one person eats?
What is the answer to the division? So each person eats ... ?

■ Challenge
Ask the children to each make up and write out two additional challenges by using the information at the head of the resource sheet. Their challenges can be used in the plenary session.

PLENARY

Use several of the additional challenges that the children have suggested and work them through with the whole class.

> **Key fact or strategy**
> Work out the operations necessary before tackling a problem involving mass.

Lesson 2

✎ Learning objectives

Mental/oral starter:
- Round decimals with two decimal places to the nearest whole number

Main teaching activities:
- Use addition, subtraction, multiplication and division to solve measurement word problems involving mass
- Explain how the problems were solved

📖 Resources

A telephone directory, photocopies of Resource Sheet 29, (A book of simple recipes should be available for the children who require an additional challenge.)

ᵃᵇᶜ Vocabulary

Decimal, decimal point, rounding, whole number, grams, weigh, measure

MENTAL/ORAL STARTER

Open up the telephone directory and read out any number or part of a number at random (leave off the zero, if there is one at the beginning of the number). Put a decimal point before the last two digits, for example, 3579 becomes 35.79 and 20143 becomes 201.43. Ask the children to respond by rounding each number to a whole number. Thus the two example numbers become 36 and 201. Repeat the exercise with numbers that have a range of numbers of digits but always give two decimal places.

MAIN ACTIVITY

Whole class, individuals, pairs

Explain to the children that they are going to be given a list of ingredients for recipes to make foods for a picnic, along with some problems related to these. Give out copies of Resource Sheet 29. Allow the children 20 minutes to work alone before teaming up with a partner to try to complete the resource sheet.

■ Support

Ask the children to begin the task in pairs. Visit them every few minutes to give them clues about how to take the next step in their work.

■ Challenge

Give the children the recipe book. They should choose a recipe, copy out the ingredients, note how many servings and then create a challenge related to the recipe.

PLENARY

Ask the children to describe the methods they used to solve the problems. Choose one of the puzzles and work it through on the board. Draw those children who found the work difficult into the discussion.

Key fact or strategy

Remember the association between grams and kilograms. Work things out a step at a time.

Supplementary activities

Mental/oral follow-up

Give the children a whole number and ask them to work out what the number might be if it has been rounded to the whole number but in fact should have one or two decimal places. Here are some examples.

If 296 is rounded one decimal place the number might be: 295.5, 295.6, 295.7, 295.8, 295.9, 296.1, 296.2, 296.3 or 296.4.

If it is a two decimal place number before rounding, it might be: 295.50, 295.51, 295.52, 295.53, 295.54, 295.55, 295.56, 295.57, 295.58, 295.59, 29.60, 296.61, 296.62, 296.63 or 296.64.

Homework

Ask the children to find recipes for two dishes they could make for their tea. They should write out the ingredients and then make up two word problems involving measures for each. These can be brought to school and worked through on the board, added to class resources or given to groups to solve as an extension activity.

Development

Use the homework to set up a measures problem workshop. Allow the children to see how many of these problems they can solve in a session. Compare methods and write them up in a classroom reference source for the class.

ICT ideas

www.counton.org (formerly the Maths 2000 website) contains a wealth of maths games. Choose from board games, number games or strategy games. The games are constantly updated.

Maths Explorer: Number (Granada Learning) includes 'Catacombs', an interactive location, with three levels of difficulty. The children have to navigate through some caves by solving various mathematical puzzles to enter an investigation in which they have to change numbers and signs to make the target number shown. One false move and the players are doomed!

Unit 7 Handling data

Framework links

7–8	10	86–101	Measures including problems	Understand area measured in square centimetres. Use formula in words for area of rectangle. Use, read and write standard metric units of mass, abbreviations. Know relationships between them. Convert larger to smaller units of mass. Suggest suitable units and equipment to estimate or measure mass. Read measurements from scales. Use all four operations to solve measurement word problems. Choose appropriate operations/calculation methods. Explain working.
		112–117	Handling data	Represent and interpret data in a line graph (for example, weight of a baby at monthly intervals from birth to one year). Recognise when points can be joined to show trends.

Setting the scene

In this unit on handling data the children have their first formal encounter with line graphs. They will have met these as pictorial representations in other subjects and in the media but now is the time that we concentrate on looking at such graphs in respect of meaning, purpose, limitations, and so on. Whilst it is important to consider when line graphs are appropriate, the emphasis here is on their interpretation, construction and the collection of data suitable for use in line graphs. Consideration of whether a graph should be a line or not is contained within discussion but the choices that need to be made about different ways of representing data come in the final unit on handling data. Continuous rather than discrete data is offered in this unit. We have adopted a developmental pattern where the children start with given line graphs, move to drawing line graphs, and finally become involved in data collection and the production of a line graph.

Starting points

The children have had experience of block graphs and bar charts. They should understand that graphs and charts are ways that we use to present information (data) visually. They should also appreciate that pictorial representation supports us in viewing information quickly and allows us to discuss that information readily.

Checking progress

- All children should be able to appreciate that a line graph helps us to understand certain kinds of data.
- Children requiring additional support will need help in understanding that intermediate points on many line graphs are assumptions rather than actual results.
- Some children will have progressed further and will be able to see that intermediate points are "best guesses". They will also appreciate that the data needs to be continuous.

Lesson 1

◥ Learning objectives

Mental/oral starter:
- Read and write whole numbers to at least 100 000

Main teaching activities:
- Represent and interpret data in a line graph

▣ Resources

An OHT of Resource Sheet 30, photocopies of Resource Sheet 31, an OHT of questions about Resource Sheet 31 (Alternatively, these can be put on the board or you can pose them orally to the whole class.)

ᵃᵇᶜ Vocabulary

Number names, line graph, point, axis, scale

MENTAL/ORAL STARTER

Write the numbers shown below on the board and ask the children to say the number. Say the word versions and ask the children to write out the number. Proceed through the selection. Add others if you wish – these might be suggestions from the children. Check a sample of the numbers that the children write and show correct numbers on the board.

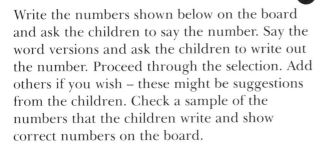

80 602	17 536

ninety-eight thousand and eleven
forty-two thousand eight hundred and forty-five

7 422	63 412

twenty-one thousand seven hundred and sixty
thirty thousand four hundred and ninety-four

59 778	72 085

MAIN ACTIVITY

Whole class, pairs

Tell the children that:
Mary bought a miracle plant in the market from a man who said that it grew like magic. When Mary planted her plant she decided to check out this claim so she measured its growth and drew a graph.

Display the OHT of Resource Sheet 30. Ask about the axes and then ask what the children think about Mary's plant. When they have made comments ask:
Do you think it is going to get any taller?

Explain that we call a graph like this a line graph.

Why did Mary join the points on the graph?

Do you think that between the points Mary is correct in drawing the line the way she has?

When you feel that the discussion has been appropriately developed tell the children that you have another graph about a plant. Give out Resource Sheet 31 to each pair and allow them a few minutes to look at what it might mean.

Now tell everyone:
Steve planted a seed in a pot and put it on the windowsill. He watered it and kept a record of how it grew. He then made this line graph.

The children have another context. Give them a few minutes to share thoughts and ideas. Pose these questions and others that you wish or that arise from the class discussion.

The seed was planted on Day 0. On which day did it start to grow?

When did it reach 3 cm in height?

What is the height that it has so far reached?

What do you expect to happen to the graph after Day 35?

Why?

■ Support

With the children, go over scale and axes and why the points are placed where they are on the graph.

■ Challenge

The children can develop some more questions about both or either of the line graphs to pose to the rest of the class.

PLENARY

Use both graphs to review scale, axes and how we place the points. Discuss why lines have been drawn between points and the fact that the lines are reasonable assumptions in these graphs.

Key fact or strategy
Line graphs are a useful way of seeing possible trends.

✎ Learning objectives
Mental/oral starter:
- Read and write whole numbers to at least 100 000

Main teaching activities:
- Represent and interpret data in a line graph

📖 Resources
Calculators, photocopies of Resource Sheet 32

ᵃᵇᶜ Vocabulary
Number names, line graph, point, axis, axes, scale, depth, approximate, experiment

MENTAL/ORAL STARTER

Give out calculators to pairs of children. Tell them that the rule for this activity is that they must press at least three and no more than five of the numeral keys on the calculator to make a three-, four- or five-digit number in the display. When they have done this, choose pairs to tell the class what number they have. Do this for a few pairs. Ask other pairs to come out and write their number on the board. The class has to say the number. Continue with this activity as you choose. If time permits you can invite the children to key in another number and share these with other pairs.

MAIN ACTIVITY

Whole class, pairs

Remind the children about the key components of line graphs: axes, scale, how we plot the points and the fact that the line between points represents a reasonable "guess" or assumption. Now give out Resource Sheet 32 to each pair. Discuss the context for the line graph. Ask them to work together to answer the questions.

■ Support
Discuss what the points mean to ensure that the children understand.

■ Challenge
They can generate further questions that could be asked and speculate on possible reasons for the rise and fall of the stream in order to help the class at the end of the lesson.

PLENARY

Go through the questions and ask different pairs for their responses. Use these to engage the class in a discussion about this particular experiment.

What might have caused these changes in depth?

Key fact or strategy
Line graphs are useful pictorial representations as they can help show change over time.

Lesson 3

Learning objectives

Mental/oral starter:
- Use doubling to multiply by 4

Main teaching activities:
- Represent and interpret data in a line graph
- Recognise when points can be joined to indicate trends

Resources

Photocopies of Resource Sheet 33 and General Resource Sheet C, atlases, sharp pencils, OHTs of graphs from previous lessons (for revision purposes), an OHT of a line graph made by using the data provided on Resource Sheet 33 or a blank graph with axes (so that the children can help you to draw the graph at the end of the lesson)

Vocabulary

Double, multiply, data, line graph, scale, axis, axes, point

MENTAL/ORAL STARTER

Quickly work through the 2 and 4 times tables. Ask an individual for a number between 10 and 100. Ask the class:
What is double that number?
What is double that answer?
What is four times the number we were given?

Repeat this type of questioning a few times. Next ask:
What connects the 2 times table and the 4 times table?

Review these tables once more. In response to the children, reinforce the fact that doubling and doubling again is the same as multiplying by four. Try a few more examples, suggested by the class, to exemplify this.

MAIN ACTIVITY

Whole class, pairs

Begin by asking:
What is a line graph?
What are the important things to think about when making a line graph?

Use an OHT that you have prepared to encourage a discussion about scale, axes, the placing of points and what the line might mean. Tell the children that in this lesson they are going to be given some data from which they need to produce a line graph. Give out atlases. Tell the children that they are going to be looking at the temperature in Chicago, USA.

Can you find where Chicago is?

When this has been done and everyone has found Chicago, make sure that all the children have a sharp pencil. Give out Resource Sheet 33 and General Resource Sheet C to pairs of children. Invite the children to try to make a line graph of these data.

■ Support

Discuss the scales on the axes and remind the children about locating and marking points.

■ Challenge

Ask the children to discuss whether the temperatures in July are high or low in comparison with where they live. Can they come up with ideas about why temperatures might differ in different places?

PLENARY

Use the OHT you have prepared or the one that just shows the axes. Go through the shape of the line graph that the children might have produced. Deal with questions about scale, and so on, as they arise. Now pose some questions:
What was the hottest/coolest day?

What was the difference between these temperatures?

If July is the hottest month what do you think your graph might look like in June/August?

What might make the temperature vary?

Key fact or strategy

To produce a line graph you need to determine a scale and mark the axes appropriately.

Lesson 4

 Learning objectives

Mental/oral starter:
- Halve any two-digit number

Main teaching activities:
- Represent and interpret data in a line graph
- Recognise when points can be joined to indicate trends

 Resources

A temperature sensor that will keep a record of temperature in the school over a 24-hour period (This should be set up prior to the lesson. If you do not have access to a sensor then you will have to fabricate information for Resource Sheet 34.), photocopies of Resource Sheet 34, a set of cards with two-digit numbers on them – sufficient for one each (The numbers can be any but include odds and evens and some from each of the tens from 10–90.), photocopies of General Resource Sheet C, OHT of General Resource Sheet C, an OHT pen

Vocabulary

Digit, halve, sensor, data, line graph, axis, point, scale

MENTAL/ORAL STARTER

Deal out the cards that you have made. The children need to look at their card and work out mentally what a half of the number is. Select individuals to show their card and say the number and its half. Ask the class if they agree. If not, ask for alternative solutions. Discuss how we can work out a half of that number in our heads. (This exercise could form a five-minute continuation exercise at other times.)

MAIN ACTIVITY

Whole class, pairs or small groups

You need to connect up the sensor 24 hours before this lesson and tell the children what you are doing. You will need to be able to give access to the readings for the children to be able to complete Resource Sheet 34. When the children have these readings (or a photocopy of ones you have fabricated) then they should attempt a line graph on General Resource Sheet C.

■ Support

Help the children with the scale and labelling of the axes.

■ Challenge

Ask the children to think of reasons why the temperature might fluctuate in the way that it has. Their suggestions can help in the plenary.

PLENARY

Draw a rough version of the graph on the board or an OHT and compare this with the versions that the children have produced. Ask them for any observations they can make about the way in which the temperature has changed over 24 hours.

Key fact or strategy

At this stage line graphs can be thought of in respect of changes over time.

Supplementary activities

Mental/oral follow-up

Get the children to collect big number facts such as the speed of light, distance to the moon, circumference of the Earth, and so on. Display these and invite the children to read out the numbers.

Continue to use cards for halving exercises. These can also be used for doubling work.

Homework

Ask the children to find any line graphs that they can in magazines, comics or newspapers and bring these in for discussion with the class.

Development

Make more use of sensors to detect environmental change, for example, noise levels and humidity. By using sensors or readings from a barometer (or daily weather maps in the newspaper) keep a record over two or three weeks and plot graphs. Weather information in newspapers can provide facts about temperatures in different locations.

ICT ideas

The data in Resource Sheets 33 and 34 could be input into a spreadsheet in order to make a line graph of continuous data. Note that though line graphs can be drwan using the temperature data on Resource Sheets 33 and 34, readings between the points cannot be relied upon. Discuss this with the children. Both graphs will show change in daytime temperature, the first over a month and the second over a day. Fluctuations throughout day and night are not shown using the Resource Sheet 33 data! You might support the children in this work by creating the structure of the spreadsheet. Leave the children to input the data values and create the graph.

Spreadsheets are a vital tool in collecting and manipulating data and include a range of graphing options. Popular applications include *Granada Spreadsheet* (Granada) and *Number Box 2* (Black Cat).

Unit 8   Money and "real-life" problems

Term   Spring 9–10

Framework links

9–10	10	40–47	Mental calculation strategies (+ and −)	Identify near doubles, for example, 1.5 + 1.6. Add/subtract multiple of 10 or 100 and adjust. Use relationship between addition and subtraction.
		48–51	Pencil and paper procedures (+ and −)	Extend written methods to addition of more than 2 integers less than 10 000, and + and − of pair of decimals both with 1 or 2 decimal places.
		82–85	Money and "real-life" problems	Use all four operations to solve money or "real-life" word problems.
		70–75	Making decisions, checking results, including using a calculator	Choose appropriate operations and calculation methods. Check by adding in reverse order, including with calculator.

Setting the scene

During the previous term the children will have had the chance to tackle some money and "real-life" problems and this unit offers them more practice. As with all the work done on money and "real-life" problems, a set of situations is offered that should connect with the children's experience and/or be interesting and entertaining. Here we engage with prices of goods including totals, differences and percentages. We offer a spatial problem and work based on a sports day.

Starting points

By now all the children should be at the stage where they are able to look at a problem and say what kinds of operation are required to solve it. This unit gives them another opportunity, not only to work out answers, but also to discuss how they worked them out.

Checking progress

- All the children should be able to give some description of how they arrived at an answer to the problems.
- Children requiring additional support may need to discuss the steps they take to reach an answer, before they carry it through.
- Some children will have progressed further. They will be able to complete the challenges with ease and go on to create more challenges of their own.

Lesson 1

◥ Learning objectives

Mental/oral starter:
- Recall addition and subtraction facts for each number up to 20

Main teaching activities:
- Use addition, subtraction, multiplication and division to solve money problems
- Explain how the answers were reached
- Use reverse operations and calculator checks to good effect

◨ Resources

A second timer that pings when time is up, make a display of sports wear and equipment (Items can be taken from the lost property box, and washed before use, and the school PE equipment cupboard should yield other items that can be put on display. A sample display is shown below.), price tags to attach to the items, a list of challenges made up by using the items on the display (These will form the main activity of the lesson.), calculators for checking

ᵃᵇᶜ Vocabulary

Price, cost, pounds, pence, buy, sell, change

MENTAL/ORAL STARTER

Remind the children that pairs of numbers that sum to, or are subtracted one from the other, make a third number are called number pairs or bonds. Call out a number between 0 and 20 and ask the children to list the addition bonds that make that number. If 12 is the number the children should say:

```
12 + 0
11 + 1
10 + 2
 9 + 3
 8 + 4
 7 + 5
 6 + 6
 5 + 7
 4 + 8,
 3 + 9
 2 + 10
 1 + 11
 0 + 12
```

Give the children another number and ask for the addition bonds. With the next number ask a pair of children to call out the bonds while the timer is set. See how long it takes and try another number and another pair of children. Ask the children to see how quick they can be. When all the addition bonds are exhausted, turn to the subtraction pairs for each number.

MAIN ACTIVITY

Whole class, pairs, small groups

Draw the children's attention to the display set up before the lesson.

Tell the children about the tasks devised for them. These should be written on the board or on pieces of paper in readiness. They should include all four operations and problems of the

following kinds:

If I buy X and Y what will I spend?

How much more/less does F cost than G?

What would 4, 5, 6, … of X cost?

If I buy Z and S what change will I have from P pounds?

If a tax of 10% is put onto U and V what will the new prices be?

Allow the children, in pairs or groups to solve the problems.

■ Support
Give the children a special set of calculations or assist them in starting out by checking their proposed methods.

■ Challenge
The children can create more challenges based on the display. These can be solved by

classmates or put up alongside the display so that the children can use them at another time. Allow the children access to calculators to check their answers.

PLENARY

Take some of the challenges. Work them out with the children's help. Explain ways in which the answer can be checked. Write up the methods of checking on the board and invite the children to carry the checks through by using their calculators.

Key fact or strategy
Checking can be done by using reverse operations. Calculators are useful for making checks on work.

Lesson 2

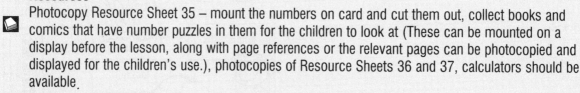

Learning objectives
Mental/oral starter:
- Add any pair of two-digit numbers

Main teaching activities:
- Use addition, subtraction, multiplication and division to solve "real-life" problems
- Explain how the answers were reached

Resources
Photocopy Resource Sheet 35 – mount the numbers on card and cut them out, collect books and comics that have number puzzles in them for the children to look at (These can be mounted on a display before the lesson, along with page references or the relevant pages can be photocopied and displayed for the children's use.), photocopies of Resource Sheets 36 and 37, calculators should be available.

Vocabulary
Times, total, price, change, cost, add, subtract, double, halve, divisible

MENTAL/ORAL STARTER

Lay the number cards out face uppermost on the front table. Ask individual children in turn to come out, pick up a pair of cards and call out any two of the numbers on the cards. The class then sum these numbers as quickly as they can. The numbers called are removed from play. When all the cards have been taken up they can all be set out again and different combination pairs can be called. Play this through several times. Discuss with the children some of the strategies that they might use, for example,

rounding the numbers to the nearest five or ten and then correcting, that is: add 10, subtract 1 for adding 9; add 5, subtract 1 for adding 4.

MAIN ACTIVITY

Whole class, individuals, small groups

Show the children the Resource Sheets 36 and 37. Explain how they can be cut up to make a small booklet as shown on next page.

Back cover   Front cover

| 2 | | 11 | 4 | | 9 | 6 | | 7 |

Pages from Resources Sheet. Reverse of each will be blank to provide pages for child to write in theit own puzzle

Show the children a booklet that is already made up. Point out the blank pages. Tell the children that you would like them to invent or find some more "quick to do" number puzzles to fill those pages.

Allow them time to each make a booklet. They then work as a group to look in the resources and try out puzzles amongst themselves until they have some that will go in the booklet. Calculators can be used to check arithmetic by carrying through calculations in reverse order.

■ **Support**

Support the children by working with them on a "Think of a number puzzle" which may have only two or three lines. They can then make the next by inserting another line into the puzzle. Simple puzzles can be very effective, for example, *What am I? I am a product in the nine times table and when halved I am in the nine times table. I have two digits that sum to nine. I am less than four times nine.* (Answer 18, 2×9)

■ **Challenge**

The children can take a turn at solving one another's puzzles.

PLENARY

Discuss with the children some of the strategies they used in trying to solve the puzzles and in creating and checking them.

> **Key fact or strategy**
> Playing with numbers can be fun.

Lesson 3

> ⬛ **Learning objectives**
> *Mental/oral starter:*
> • Subtract any pair of two-digit numbers
> *Main teaching activities:*
> • Use addition, subtraction, multiplication and division to solve money problems
> • Use addition, subtraction, multiplication and division to solve "real-life" problems
> • Explain how the answers were reached
>
> 📖 **Resources**
> Two dice (dice 1 numbered 1–6 and dice 2 numbered 0, 5, 6, 7, 8, 9), photocopies of Resource Sheet 38
>
> **a,c** **Vocabulary**
> **b** Takings, cost, balance, total

MENTAL/ORAL STARTER

Throw dice 1 four times, to yield four digits. Make two numbers from these and then subtract the lower number from the higher one, for example, if 1, 4, 6 and 2 are thrown, two possible two-digit numbers are 46 and 21. The subtraction using these numbers would then be 46 – 21 and the answer is 25. Follow this procedure again and again. Ask individual

children to make the two numbers and carry through the subtraction.

Throw dices 1 and 2 twice each, in order to accrue four digits. Do this several times. Finally throw dice 2 four times to obtain four digits from the list 0, 5, 6, 7, 8, 9. Do this several times. Allow the children to combine the digits and make the subtractions as before.

MAIN ACTIVITY

Whole class, individuals, pairs, small groups

Give each child a small piece of card. Ask them to write their name on it and then draw on it a quick picture of an object, event or stall that they associate with a village sports day, fete or gala. Alongside the picture, ask them to write a sum of money and a number associated with their picture.

A drawing may be a swingboat, the sum of money £1.50 or £90, and the number 23. The former may be the cost of the ride, or the total takings on the day and the latter the number of adults who went on the ride.

Ask individual children to show their cards, talk about the picture and explain the figures they have attached. Use the figures to create challenges that the class can work through on the board. Do this for three or four of the cards. Collect in the cards so that they can be used for further development work.

Give each child a copy of Resource Sheet 38. Allow them time to try to solve the money and number problems there, wtiting the answers in the workbooks.

■ **Support**

Help the children to choose which problem to tackle first by reading the problems through with them and talking about how they can be tackled. On this resource sheet the last challenge might prove to be the easiest to carry through.

■ **Challenge**

Ask the children to use the data on the resource sheet to devise and carry through two more challenges.

PLENARY

Hand out calculators and ask the children to check their working. Discuss and solve any discrepancies.

Key fact or strategy

Think logically about a challenge before tackling it.

Supplementary activities

Mental/oral follow-up

Play "What's missing" by giving the children one two-digit number from an addition, along with the answer, and asking, "What's missing?" If the first number is 27 and the answer is 102, the missing number is 75. Check that the missing number has two digits.

Carry through a similar set of puzzles that are subtractions.

Homework

Invite the children to continue to find or devise number puzzles to put into their "Think of a number puzzle" booklets made in Lesson 2. The children could complete the chsllenges on Resource Sheet 38 if there was insufficient time in the lesson.

Development

Use the picture cards the children drew in Lesson 3 to create a frieze or display of village event challenges. The numbers and sums of money they have written down can be incorporated into the puzzles, and information on different cards can be compared to give the children the chance to carry through all four operations.

ICT ideas

Zoombinis Maths Journey (Learning Company) offers a wealth of multi-layered problem-solving activities with many offering up to four difficulty levels. The problems and puzzles incorporate aspects of thinking skills and strategy, and build into a comprehensive problem-solving package.

Breakaway Maths CD-ROM (available through Nelson Thornes) is designed for children who are experiencing difficulties with their mathematics work. The CD-ROM includes some stimulating investigations based around the context of a theme park and could be used to develop children's confidence and mathematical capabilities.

Unit 9 Money and "real-life" problems

Term	Summer 2–3

Framework links

2–3	10	52–57	Understanding × and ÷	Express a quotient as a fraction, or as a decimal when dividing a whole number by 2, 4, 5, 10 or when dividing £ and pence. Round up or down depending on the context. Use relationship between × and ÷.
		60–65	Mental calculation strategies (× and ÷)	Use known facts and place value to multiply and divide mentally. Extend written methods to TU × TU (long multiplication).
		66–69	Pencil and paper procedures (× and ÷)	Use all four operations to solve money or "real-life" problems, including percentages.
		82–85	Money and "real-life" problems	Choose appropriate operations/calculation methods. Explain working.
		70–75	Making decisions and checking results including using a calculator	Check results.

Setting the scene

Children need plenty of practice in working through realistic problems as this kind of applied mathematics is essential for success in everyday life. Unit 9 builds on the copious experience they have had in Units 1, 4, 5 and 8.

Starting points

The chief aim of this unit is to increase the children's confidence, not only in choosing how to tackle a problem and in justifying their choice of method but also in carrying through appropriate checks, without help.

Checking progress

- All the children should be able to choose appropriate operations, explain what they have done, and tackle a check on their own results.
- Children requiring additional support may need to have clues about how to relate the steps they take to reach an answer. They will benefit from being given an array of possible checks from which they can choose.
- Some children will have progressed further and will not only create new challenges but will also check the work of others.

Lesson 1

 Learning objectives

Mental/oral starter:
- Multiply two-digit numbers by 4, by doubling

Main teaching activities:
- Choose which of these operations to use to solve money problems – addition, subtraction, multiplication and division
- Explain how the problems were worked out
- Check results

Resources

Photocopies of Resource Sheet 39, access to a selection of books (preferably with prices on)

Vocabulary

Two-digit, multiply, double, price, cost, difference, change

MENTAL/ORAL STARTER

Write up a two-digit number on the board. Write in × 4. Suggest to the children that if they double the number (that is multiply it by 2) and then double that, they will arrive at the answer. Here is an example worked through.

I am going to write a two-digit number on the board: 46.

46×4

If we want to multiply 46 by 4, we can say, what is double 46, and then double that to get an answer.

$46 \times 2 = 92 \qquad 92 \times 2 = 184$

Try this out many times by writing up the two-digit numbers and asking the children to do the calculation in their heads. If some numbers prove tricky, work through the two steps with them.

MAIN ACTIVITY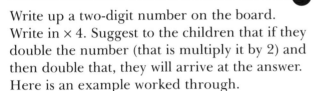

Whole class, individuals, pairs

Take up a book from the classroom bookshelf. Look for the price on the back or sleeve. If it has no price, assign it one and then ask the children:
What would two copies of this book cost? ... five copies? ... ten copies?

Take up another book and create challenges involving them both. Include the following ideas:

- combined price
- difference in price
- cost if half price
- change if £10 or £20 is offered.

Give every child a copy of Resource Sheet 39. Allow the children time to try the puzzles. They should see how many they can solve alone, before working with a partner and writing answers into their workbooks.

■ Support

After they have tried to solve these puzzles themselves, allow the children to each join a pair who are getting along particularly well. They should then be helped to do the necessary calculations.

■ Challenge

Ask the children to devise ways of checking the answers to the calculations.

PLENARY

Ask the children to supply the answers to the puzzles on Resource Sheet 39 and describe a method for checking their answers. Work through the checks with the children. Give calculators to those children who needed extra support during the main session so that they can do the calculator checks of the answers.

Key fact or strategy

Carrying through checks of the answers obtained is important.

Lesson 2

◣ Learning objectives
Mental/oral starter:
* Use halving to divide two-digit numbers by 4

Main teaching activities:
* Choose which of these operations to use to solve "real-life" problems – addition, subtraction, multiplication and division
* Explain how the problems were worked out
* Check results

◆ Resources
Photocopy Resource Sheet 40 for the mental/oral starter (This needs to be done well before the lesson, so that the number cards can be cut up in readiness. Create a blank card for each child in the class.)

(Note: Before this lesson takes place the children need to be involved in a traffic census at the school gate. Under supervision, and as a group at a time, they should collect some census data. Resource Sheet 41 is set out ready for a tally and may be appropriate. Collate the census data and compile some challenges that involve two- and three-digit numbers. If the census results yield only small numbers they can be multiplied to give bigger figures, for example, if 3 motor bikes go by in an hour that might mean 18 in a school day, 90 in a school week, and so on.)

Vocabulary
Divide, halve, census, tally, data

MENTAL/ORAL STARTER

Fold up one of the number cards so that the number at the top is revealed. Call it out. Say that it can be divided by four by halving it and halving it again. Invite the children to halve the number. Reveal the answer by folding out the next flap of the card. Halve it again and reveal the third flap. Now ask:
What is ... (the start number) divided by 4?

The children should call out the number on the final flap.

Try this exercise with a couple more of the number cards from Resource Sheet 40 before giving each child a blank number card. Ask the children to write a two-digit number at the top, halve that number, halve it again and write in the answer each time. Invite individual children to show their cards to the class. All the cards can be collected in and used in the mental/oral follow-up at the end of the unit.

MAIN ACTIVITY

Whole class, individuals, pairs or small groups

Write on the board some number challenges based on the census data that the children have collected. (This should be collated and set out ready for their use before the lesson.)

The challenges can be tackled by individuals, pairs or groups, according to the nature of the challenge.

■ Support
The children may require regular focused questioning from you to carry their work forward.

■ Challenge
The children may be able to create fresh challenges by using the census data.

PLENARY

Go through the puzzles that you set out for the children to solve. Invite different pairs or groups to suggest how the answers to each problem might be checked.

Key fact or strategy
Real data can be used to generate problems to solve.

Lesson 3

Learning objectives

Mental/oral starter:
- Partition to multiply by 2, 5 or 10, and use tests of divisibility

Main teaching activities:
- Choose which of these operations to use to solve money or "real-life" problems – addition, subtraction, multiplication and division
- Explain how the problems were worked out
- Check results

Resources

Obtain information, posters and booklets about local swimming clubs (If there is a club run by the school, record the details of arrangements and membership of this too. This data provides information for discussion in the lesson.), photocopies of Resource Sheet 42

Vocabulary

Two-digit, tens, units, multiplication, divisible, partition, cost, total, buy, pay

MENTAL/ORAL STARTER

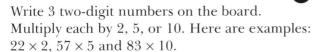

Write 3 two-digit numbers on the board. Multiply each by 2, 5, or 10. Here are examples: 22×2, 57×5 and 83×10.

Remind the children that we can partition a number into tens and units before multiplying to make the multiplication easier.

We can say 22×2 is 20×2 plus 2×2 and this gives $40 + 4$. Therefore, the answer is 44.

Work through the other two examples. Write up another two-digit number. Ask individual children to multiply the number by 2, then 5, then 10 and to explain how they partition the number to do so. Try this out with some more examples.

Ask the children how they can tell by looking at a number whether it will be divisible by 2, 5 or 10. Work through their ideas by using actual examples to check them out. The children should offer the following:

- If the last digit is even or 0, the number can be divided exactly by 2.
- If the last digit is 5 or 0, the number can be divided exactly by 5.
- If the last digit is 0, the number can be divided exactly by 10.
- A number ending in 0 can be divided by 2, 5 or 10.

Finally ask the children which of an array of numbers, such as 111, 630, 46, 55, 210, 14, can be divided exactly by 2, 5 or 10.

MAIN ACTIVITY

Whole class, individuals, pairs

Talk generally to the children about membership of local swimming clubs. Use the information that you have collected. The children can share their experiences of such clubs. Establish answers to questions such as the following:

How much does it cost to join?

What is a season ticket?

What facilities are available?

When can you swim?

Give each child a copy of Resource Sheet 42. Ask the children to find answers to the money and "real-life" problems found there. After some minutes working alone, and if you feel it is appropriate, they can work with a partner to complete the work on the resource sheet.

■ Support

Take the puzzles one at a time and help the children to decide what it is that they want to find out, the methods they are going to use and the steps to take to reach an answer.

■ Challenge

By using what they know about their own swimming club, or some of the information you have secured about local clubs, the children can write a small information page about a club and create some puzzles to attach. These can be used in development sessions.

51

PLENARY

Ask the children which of the problems on Resource Sheet 42 they found most difficult. Work these out as a class, looking at possible methods, quickest methods and points at which errors might occur. Allow individuals to suggest the best ways of checking all the problems on the resource sheet.

Key fact or strategy
Data from our own lives can yield problems to solve – we can apply what we learn in mathematics to our everyday lives.

Supplementary activities

Mental/oral follow-up

Make up a bingo number box with two- and three-digit numbers on pieces of card. Divide the class into three groups: the twos, the fives, and the tens. Hold up a number and ask the children to stand up, or put their hand up, if the number is divisible by their number. For the number 282, only the "twos" should put up their hands. For the number 60 all three groups should put up their hands, while for the number 47 no-one should respond.

Homework

Give each child a copy of Resource Sheet 43. Invite them to take it home and create a swimwear shop. They can stick prices onto the resource sheet or cut out the items there and stick them onto card. These can be placed in a shallow box which becomes the "shop". They then need to make up ten problems related to the items. These should include totals, price differences, reductions and change.

Development

Use the completed homework to set up at least two swimwear problem workshops. The children can try to solve one another's puzzles. A group of children can be nominated "checkers" to use methods like the following to check out the answers people are getting:
- inverse operations
- equivalent calculations
- rounding
- the predicted outcomes when summing or finding the difference between odd and even numbers.

ICT ideas

Percentages Games (Sherston Software) provides helpful practice and consolidation of children's work in this area in a problem-solving context – for example, children must use their knowledge of percentages of a whole to complete the toppings on a pizza order.

Unit 9 **Supplementary activities**

Unit 10 Handling data

Framework links

6	8	112–117	Handling data	Solve a problem by representing and interpreting data in bar line charts: axis in 2s, 5s, 10s, 20s, 100s. Discuss cases where intermediate points have no meaning and cases where points may be joined to show trend.
				Find the mode and calculate the range of a set of data.
		70–71	Using a calculator	Use a computer to compare different presentations of the same data.

Setting the scene

Handling data is a key skill in much of what we do in everyday life. Whether it be making decisions about the probable outcome of events or making judgements through comparisons, we are all using data handling skills. In this unit the children continue their work on understanding aspects of pictorial representation and the emphasis is on bar line graphs/charts. The opportunity is taken to explore ideas connected to discrete and continuous data through discussion of when you may and may not join the tops of bar lines. This work and earlier work on bar charts and line graphs is consolidated through two lessons based round the use of the computer. This computer work is intended to do two things: give the children an appreciation of what pictorial representation is possible; encourage them to make reasoned choices about which available representation to use. The unit ends with more work on modal average and range.

Starting points

The children should know about scale, axes and have had experience of drawing and interpreting bar charts and some line graphs. The children have had an introduction to mode and range. They should also be used to using the computer. In lessons 4 and 5 the children need to use spreadsheets on the computer. If they have not had experience of this before, give them the opportunity to work with simple spreadsheets before the lessons.

Checking progress

- All children should be able to plot points on a chart or graph.
- Children requiring additional support will need help in understanding why we cannot always join points at the top of bar lines.
- Some children will have progressed further and will be able to make reasoned choices about scale and the best form of representation. They will have clear recall of the meaning of mode and range.

Lesson 1

Learning objectives

Mental/oral starter:
- Recall addition and subtraction facts up to 20

Main teaching activities:
- Solve a problem by representing and interpreting data in bar line charts
- Discuss cases where intermediate points have no meaning and cases where points may be joined to show a trend

Resources

Photocopies of Resource Sheet 44, an OHT of Resource Sheet 44, rulers and sharp pencils or coloured pencils

Vocabulary

Bar line, chart, graph, data, scale, axis, axes, points

MENTAL/ORAL STARTER

Use this lesson to revisit addition and subtraction common number bonds. Use questions like these to test the children's knowledge:

What do X and Y make?

What is the total if we add A and B?

What is the difference between X and Y?

Give me four pairs of numbers that sum to N.

Give me three ways of making 5 by using subtraction.

MAIN ACTIVITY

Whole class, pairs

Begin by asking:

What can you tell me about bar line charts?

Use the responses to outline the key characteristics of such a chart. Tell the children that you are a keen football fan and that you support Hightown Rovers. You have been looking at the number of spectators at some recent matches and you want the children to draw a graph of these for you. Organise the children into pairs and ensure that they have rulers and pencils or coloured pencils. Give out Resource Sheet 44. Review the scale and the meaning of each axis. Ask the children to draw a chart.

■ Support

Help the children to locate the data for the first match on the chart.

■ Challenge

They can tackle this question: *If tickets are £10 each how much did Hightown raise in these matches?*

PLENARY

Invite different pairs to show their charts and help you to make your own on the OHT that you have prepared. Engage the children in a discussion of how the chart is made. This should involve mention of scales, axes and what bar lines are.

Can we join the tops of these lines to make a line graph?

Encourage the children to explain why this is not possible in this case.

> **Key fact or strategy**
> It is not always possible to connect the tops of bar line charts because intermediate points have no meaning.

55

Lesson 2

✎ Learning objectives
Mental/oral starter:
- Add any pair of two-digit numbers

Main teaching activities:
- Solve a problem by representing and interpreting data in bar line charts
- Discuss cases where intermediate points have no meaning and cases where points may be joined to show a trend

📖 Resources
Photocopies of Resource Sheet 45, an OHT of Resource Sheet 45, rulers and sharp pencils or coloured pencils, an OHT of the "Addition number grid" (see below) or write the grid on the board

ᵃᵇᶜ Vocabulary
Bar line, chart, graph, data, scale, axis, axes, points

MENTAL/ORAL STARTER

Use the OHT or the board drawing that you have prepared of the grid shown here.

Addition number grid

56	73	39
91	18	60
24	35	42

Choose pairs of numbers at random and ask the children to tell you the total in each case.

MAIN ACTIVITY

Whole class, then pairs

Tell the children that in this lesson they are going to be drawing another bar line chart. Tell them:
This time you are going to have to mark in the axes yourselves.

As necessary talk about what it means to think about scale and decide what each axis represents. If it helps, show your OHT of Resource Sheet 45 to stimulate discussion but do not mark in axes at this stage. When the children seem ready, organise them into pairs. Check that they have the equipment needed. Give out copies of Resource Sheet 45. Ask the pairs to put the correct numbers/information on the axes and then draw a bar line chart.

■ Support
Help the children with marking out the axes appropriately.

■ Challenge
Ask the children to think of two extra questions and work out the answers so that the questions can be put to the class in a later session.

PLENARY

Use the OHT you have prepared. Ask the children to instruct you on how to mark the axes and draw the bar lines.

Can we join the tops of the lines in this case?

Encourage the children to explain why it is possible to do this on this occasion. Collect in the charts that the children have drawn for evaluation.

Key fact or strategy
In some cases it is appropriate to join the tops of the bar lines to indicate trends.

Lesson 3

Learning objectives
Mental/oral starter:
- Subtract any pair of two-digit numbers

Main teaching activities:
- Solve a problem by representing and interpreting data in bar line charts
- Discuss cases where intermediate points have no meaning and cases where points may be joined to show a trend

Resources
Photocopies of Resource Sheets 46, an OHT of Resource Sheet 46, rulers and sharp pencils or coloured pencils, an OHT of the "Subtraction number grid" (see below) or write the grid on the board

Vocabulary
Bar line, chart, graph, data, scale, axis, axes, points

MENTAL/ORAL STARTER

Use the OHT or the board drawing that you have prepared of the grid shown here.

Subtraction number grid

44	38	71
98	26	65
22	14	53

Choose pairs of numbers at random and ask the children to tell you the difference in each case.

MAIN ACTIVITY

Whole class, individuals or pairs

Tell the children:
I have another bar line chart for you today. This time I want you to show me just how much you know about making such charts.

Give out copies of Resource Sheet 46 to either individuals or pairs. Make sure that all the children have rulers and pencils. Let them get on with the task. Respond as necessary but note that the intention in this lesson is to give you an opportunity to watch and assess how well the children are progressing in this area.

Allow discussion of the last question on the resource sheet.

■ Support
Give the children help on demand but stand back rather than elaborate on each occasion.

■ Challenge
Can the children pose other questions about this chart?

PLENARY

Collect in the work. Use your OHT to review how to approach the task. Encourage the children to tell you how they did this. Ask the question about joining the tops of the lines and why it would be meaningless to do so.

Key fact or strategy
To construct a bar line chart you need to think about scale and whether there is meaning to intermediate points.

Lesson 4

◤ Learning objectives
Mental/oral starter:
- Multiply or divide whole numbers up to 10 000 by 10 and 100

Main teaching activities:
- Use a computer to compare different presentations of the same data

◢ Resources
Photocopies of Resource Sheet 46, 47 and 48, a computer (or suite of computers for the whole class) with a spreadsheet package such as *Granada Spreadsheet*. (You might wish to prepare the number of rows) and columns for the children if they have had little experience of preparing data on a spreadsheet.

ᵃᵇᶜ Vocabulary
Data, spreadsheet, column, row, function, takings

MENTAL/ORAL STARTER

In this session concentrate on multiplying and dividing by 10. Here are some numbers written as digits and words to give to the children. Write the numeral examples on the board and say the others aloud.

---

8 053	2 146	7 301

one thousand and six hundred and fifty-nine

641

five thousand four hundred and ninety-two

76   131

three thousand and six

four thousand eight hundred and eighty-eight

What is this multiplied by 10?
What is this divided by 10?

MAIN ACTIVITY

Whole class, pairs or small groups

Ask the children what they understand by a spreadsheet. Correct any misconceptions and give out copies of Resource Sheet 47 to pairs or small groups.

Invite the children to enter the data from Resource Sheet 47 into a spreadsheet on the computer.

Then ask the following questions:

1. *What was the best-selling snack in the shop over the whole week?*

2. *Which item sold most on Thursday?*

Explain that the spreadsheet shows the amount of money taken for each item, and that they need to total various columns to help them answer the first question. They then need to prepare a chart to present their answers.

Allow discussion of both questions and schedule time within a computer suite so that all children have the opportunity to prepare and present the data.

▪ Support
Resource Sheet 48 shows how to use the sum function and to make a chart or graph using *Granada Spreadsheet*. This might be useful for children who have had little experience of using spreadsheets. For other spreadsheet packages, you will need to amend the instructions slightly.

▪ Challenge
Can the children pose other questions about the data and present their answers by using appropriate graphing functions?

PLENARY

Allow each of the groups/pairs to explain their work. Encourage the children to tell you how they prepared the data and why they selected particular graphing functions.

Key fact or strategy
Bar charts are suitable for both questions as the data is discrete. Line graphs or bar line charts are not appropriate here.

Lesson 5

✎ Learning objectives
Mental/oral starter:
- Multiply or divide whole numbers up to 10 000 by 10 and 100

Main teaching activities:
- Use a computer to compare different presentations of the same data

📖 Resources
Photocopies of Resource Sheet 48, a computer (or suite of computers for the whole class) with a spreadsheet package such as *Granada Spreadsheet*. Photocopies of Resource Sheets 44, 45 or 46 with the children's prepared bar line charts.

abc Vocabulary
Input, spreadsheet, bar line chart, row, column, function

MENTAL/ORAL STARTER 🕙

Provide some numbers, as in the last lesson, but this time concentrate on multiplying and dividing by 100. Here are some more numbers written as digits and words to give the children. Write the numeral examples on the board and speak the others.

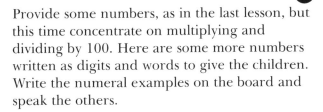

| 462 | 7 969 | 411 |

seven thousand two hundred and fifty-five

three thousand and three hundred and twenty-four

5 750

four thousand and twelve

two thousand seven hundred and sixteen

9 814   8 468

What is this divided by 100?
What is this divided by 100?

MAIN ACTIVITY 🕙35

Whole class, pairs or small groups

Tell the children:
Today, we are going to look again at the bar line charts you prepared in previous lessons. You will enter the same data onto a spreadsheet and then prepare charts to present the data.

Give out copies of Resource Sheet 48 to pairs or small groups if the children need a reminder of how to input data or prepare a chart. Make sure that they understand that they are using the computer to compare the presentation of the data with the bar line charts they drew in previous lessons.

Allow discussion of both questions. Schedule time within a computer suite, where available, so that all children have the opportunity to prepare and present the data.

▪ Support
Help the children by setting up the rows and columns for the spreadsheets and support the children in by using the graphing functions of the spreadsheet.

▪ Challenge
Can the children pose other questions about the charts using the spreadsheet functions?

PLENARY 🕙10

Allow each of the groups/pairs to explain their work. Encourage the children to tell you how they prepared the data and why they selected particular graphing functions. Ask them to explain the differences between preparing the bar line charts by using paper and pencil and preparing the data on computer.

Key fact or strategy
Remind the children to think about the meaning of the intermediate points of the bar line chart and to think about the scale of the charts.

Lesson 6

📎 Learning objectives

Mental/oral starter:
• Recall facts in the 7 times table

Main teaching activity:
• Find the mode and calculate the range of a set of data

📖 Resources
Photocopies of Resource Sheet 49

Vocabulary
Mode, range, tally, data

MENTAL/ORAL STARTER

Work through the whole of the 7 times table and write this on the board as the children tell you. Go through the table on the board as a quick "chant". Rub out the table and ask the children which of the 7 times table makes these products. Choose a random selection such as 28, 63, 21, 7, 49, 35, and so on.

MAIN ACTIVITY

Whole class, pairs or small groups

Ask the children to tell you what they recall about the work that they did earlier in the year on mode and range. Through their responses reinforce what these terms mean.

What do we mean by "tally"?

Invite someone to show the class an example of a tally based on, say, the number of girls in the class.

Group the children then give them copies of Resource Sheet 49. Read through the introduction and tell the children that you want them to convert the tally to numbers and answer the questions.

■ Support

Give a few examples of sets of numbers. Remind the children how to work out the mode and the range.

■ Challenge

The children can use the data shown here to extend the work to some larger quantities.

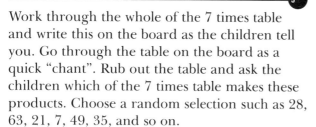

Year	Chicks hatched
1	⊦⊦⊦⊦ ⊦⊦⊦⊦ ‖
2	⊦⊦⊦⊦ ⊦⊦⊦⊦ ⊦⊦⊦⊦ ‖‖
3	⊦⊦⊦⊦ ⊦⊦⊦⊦ ‖‖‖
4	⊦⊦⊦⊦ ⊦⊦⊦⊦ ⊦⊦⊦⊦ ‖‖
5	⊦⊦⊦⊦ ⊦⊦⊦⊦ ⊦⊦⊦⊦ ‖

PLENARY

Ask the children for the mode and range. Check the groups who got this and make a mental note of any children who had difficulties. Work with these children before the next lesson.

What is your prediction about how long William will have to wait?
Why?

The mode is 4 so one might estimate that the robin appears about every 15 minutes. The range suggests something between 20 minutes and 6 minutes so William might not have to wait 15 minutes.

Key fact or strategy
The mode and range can help us to make predictions.

Lesson 7

■ **Learning objectives**
Mental/oral starter:
• Recall facts in the 9 times table
Main teaching activity:
• Find the mode and calculate the range of a set of data

■ **Resources**
Photocopies of Resource Sheet 50, BT telephone directory, current call charges (There is a "**free**fone" number in the directory where charges can be obtained.)

■ **Vocabulary**
Mode, range, data

MENTAL/ORAL STARTER

As in the last lesson, work through the whole of a table. In this lesson use the 9 times table. Write the table on the board as the children tell it to you. Go through the table as a quick "chant". Rub out the table. Ask the children which of the multiplications in the 9 times table makes certain products. Choose a random selection: 90, 18, 45, 54, 81, and so on.

MAIN ACTIVITY

Whole class, pairs

Ask the children:
Do you use the phone much?

Does anyone ever complain about how long you are on the phone?

Tell them that there is a girl called Gemma who is having some problems with her dad about her use of the phone. Can the class help her? Give out copies of Resource Sheet 50 and ask pairs to work together to find the mode and range before answering Gemma's question.

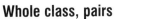

■ **Support**
Give a list of single figures with repeats to remind the children that mode means most often. Use these figures to demonstrate how we calculate range.

■ **Challenge**
Ask the children to work out the cost of the calls. Assume that they are local. What if Stacey was in France? Encourage the children to read the charging pages in the telephone directory.

PLENARY

Begin by asking:
What is the mode? ... and the range?

What is your advice to Gemma?

Why?

Discuss the reasons for the choices made. The mode is certainly better from Gemma's point of view! If there is time, talk a little about how phone charges are made in respect of local, national and international calls. If the children have access to a mobile phone, what are the charges?

> **Key fact or strategy**
> Both the mode and the range are important to know.

61

Lesson 8

Learning objectives
Mental/oral starter:
• Partition to multiply by 2, 5 and 10
Main teaching activity:
• Find the mode and calculate the range of a set of data

Resources
An OHT of Resource Sheet 51, OHT pens (three colours needed), photocopies of Resource Sheet 52

Vocabulary
Data, mode, range, test

MENTAL/ORAL STARTER

Display the OHT of Resource Sheet 51. Ask the children to help you to circle the numbers that are divisible by 2 in one colour, by 5 in another, and by 10 in the final colour. Are there any numbers with one circle, two, all three?

MAIN ACTIVITY

Whole class, pairs

Review what the children know about mode and range. Tell them that:
In this lesson you are going to be looking at a teacher's favourite topic – tests!

Give out copies of Resource Sheet 52 to pairs of children. Give a broad overview of the context and the task before asking the children to answer the questions.

■ Support
Help the children to reorder scores from highest to lowest or vice versa.

■ Challenge
If Eric had scored 55 for science and 65 for maths, and Tamsin's scores had been 55 for science and 56 for maths, how would this change the range and mode for each set of scores?

PLENARY

What is the mode and range for science?

What are these for mathematics?

Check that everyone agrees on these results.

Can you make any suggestions about which of the tests the children might have found more difficult?

Discuss the respective ranges and compare modes. This could indicate that most children were more at ease with the mathematics test but we would need more information to be sure of our ideas.

Key fact or strategy
Using the mode and range can help to make comparisons between sets of data.

Supplementary activities

Mental/oral follow-up

Continue giving the children practice with the multiplication tables, particularly 7, 8 and 9. Ask the children to make different sets of pairs of numbers that sum to, or that the differences will make, given target numbers. Do this to 100.

Homework

Give the children copies of Resource Sheet 53. Snack cheese biscuits are sold by weight so, depending on the size of each biscuit, the number in a pack can vary. Tell the children that the biscuits on the sheet come from six different packs. The mode is 4 and the range is 7. Can they suggest the contents for the five packs that will fit this mode and range? One possibility is 5, 7, 7, 7, 8, and 9.

Development

Use materials such as travel brochures which have temperature charts for different locations (some atlases also have such information) to further explore pictorial representations.

There is school data in attendance and dinner registers that can be used for both the production of charts and mode and range discussions.

By using Resource Sheet 53 as a starting point, you could double the number of biscuits and get bar line charts drawn of the contents of packs.

ICT ideas

If the children are to see the potential applications for a spreadsheet, they need to use them over a number of years. Using the spreadsheet as a simple graph-drawing tool (as is the case with Lessons 4 and 5) offers a good introduction to the spreadsheet program as it is an extremely efficient tool for accepting data and displaying it in graphical format. As they gain in confidence, the children may begin to play and experiment with calculations and start to use formulas (such as the Sum formula used in Lesson 5). You can help the children to use the spreadsheet as a problem-solving tool by applying standard strategies such as breaking a problem down into manageable bits.

Unit 11 Measures problems

Framework links

8–10	15	102–111	Shape and space	Recognise reflective symmetry in regular polygons. Complete symmetrical patterns with two lines of symmetry at right angles. Reflect shapes in mirror parallel to one side. Recognise where shape will be after translation.
		76–81	Reasoning about shapes	Make and investigate a general statement about shapes. Use timetables. Know and use relationship between units of time.
		86–101	Measures including problems	Use, read and write standard metric units of capacity, including abbreviations and pint, gallon. Know and use relationships between them. Convert larger to smaller units of capacity, including gallons to pints. Suggest suitable units and equipment to estimate or measure capacity. Read measurements from scales. Use all four operations to solve measurement word problems, including time. Choose appropriate operations/calculation methods. Explain working.

Setting the scene

As this is the last unit of this kind in the year, there are opportunities for revision as well as new work. The children have the opportunity to solve problems related to capacity, in association with length and mass.

Starting points

During this year the children have worked with all the major units of measurement of length and mass. They have worked on hours and minutes and the 24-hour clock.

Checking progress

- All children should show confidence in dealing with the relationships between common units of measurement of length, capacity and mass. They should be able to identify which operations are necessary to solve problems and attempt to solve word problems that involve measures of length, capacity and mass. They should be able to attempt to solve problems involving time and describe their approaches.
- Children requiring additional support will need to be reminded of the relationships between common units of measurement of length, capacity and mass. They may need support in remembering how measures of time are associated with one another and with interpreting a complex timetable.
- Some children will have progressed further. They can describe and explain their approaches in solving word problems involving measures of length, capacity, mass and time.

Lesson 1

✎ Learning objectives
Mental/oral starter:
- Put into order decimals with the same number of decimal places

Main teaching activities:
- Use addition, subtraction, multiplication and division to solve word problems involving measures of length and capacity

📖 Resources
One photocopy of Resource Sheet 54 backed onto card and cut into number cards, a metre stick marked up in centimetres, a 30 cm rule marked in millimetres, a measuring jug showing millilitres, photocopies of Resource Sheet 55

🔤 Vocabulary
Centimetres, metres, millilitres, litres

MENTAL/ORAL STARTER

Shuffle the decimal number cards. Give each child a card. Ask the child with the star on their card to begin. (This is the lowest number.) Either ask the children to line up in number order or ask them to put their hands up and call out their number in ascending order.

Collect in the cards, shuffle them and deal them out again. Ask the children to work in descending order this time. Begin with 99.01. The game can be played two or three more times.

MAIN ACTIVITY

Whole class, pairs

Remind the children of some of the measurements in common use. Display the selection of measuring instruments to stimulate the discussion. Show the metre stick marked up in centimetres and a 30 cm rule marked in millimetres. Talk about these units. Check that the children know the association between them. Point out the measurements on the side of the measuring jug and establish that there are 1 000 ml in one litre.

Try out a couple of example word problems with the children. Here are two examples with some suggested key questions.

There are 200 ml in a glass of breakfast juice. If the jug holds 1½ litres of juice, how many full glasses can be poured from it? How much juice is left over?

What do we need to do first? (convert litres to ml)

What kind of operation(s) will solve the problem? (division and then multiplication)

Here is one way of solving the problem.

1½ litres = 1 500 ml

1 500 ml ÷ 200 ml = 7 with 100 ml left over

Cleo uses 1.40 m cloth to make cushions and 6.26 m to make curtains. The bolt of cloth she uses is 10 m long. How much cloth is left over?

What kind of calculation do we need to do? (addition and then subtraction)

Can we estimate the answer?

Give pairs of children copies of Resource Sheet 55. Invite them to work out the answers to the problems in their workbooks.

■ Support
Ask the children to work out what kinds of calculation they will need to do first. Then they should try the arithmetic and compare answers with one another. Talk through each problem with them. "Think aloud" in order to give the children strategies.

■ Challenge
Ask the pairs of children to join in groups to calculate how many different methods they used to solve the problems.

PLENARY

Take example problems from Resource Sheet 55 and invite individual children to say how they went about solving them.

Key fact or strategy
Converting cm to m and ml to l, and vice versa, is necessary to solve measures problems.

Lesson 2

Learning objectives
Mental/oral starter:
- Use doubling or halving to multiply or divide two-digit numbers by 4

Main teaching activities:
- Use addition, subtraction, multiplication and division to solve word problems involving measures of mass and capacity
- Explain how they worked them out

Resources
Card strips as shown in the mental/oral starter, a kitchen balance marked in metric, a measuring jug showing millilitres, photocopies of Resource Sheet 56 (If required the following packaging can be assembled to provide support for the children who need it: a plain flour bag, a bicarbonate of soda container with a medicine or other 5 ml spoon, a ground ginger container, a butter wrapper – wrapped around a cuboid box to mimic the shape of a pack of butter, a sugar bag, a golden syrup jar, a measuring jug or cylinder, an egg box.), a book of simple cake and biscuit recipes (or a few of these recipes copied out onto card)

Vocabulary
Two-digit, halve, double, mass, weight, grams, kilograms, capacity, millilitres, litres, operation

MENTAL/ORAL STARTER

Give each child a strip of card. Ask them to write a two-digit number at the top in the centre. They should then show the halving and doubling steps that can occur when this number is divided by 4 or multiplied by 4. Here is an example strip when complete.

$$\div 4 \leftarrow 60 \rightarrow \times 4$$

$\div 2$	$\div 2$	$\times 2$	$\times 2$
15	30	120	240

MAIN ACTIVITY

Whole class, individuals, pairs

Weigh a few items on the kitchen balance. Call out the readings in grams and kilograms. Discuss the association between these measurements. Revise measures of capacity, as indicated in Lesson 1, by pointing out the measurements on the side of the measuring jug and establish that there are 1 000 ml in one litre.

Use Resource Sheet 56 to write out the ingredients on the board. Discuss with the children how they might solve the first challenge, namely to work out the ingredients list to make 30 rather than 20 gingerbread people. Establish the kinds of operations

necessary. Write out how each quantity is determined.

Give each child a copy of Resource Sheet 56. Invite the children to tackle the challenges set out there by beginning with the second challenge. When they reach challenge 4 (about Susan and her friends) they should find a partner, discuss how they solved the earlier calculations and then work on subsequent ones together.

■ Support
Set out the wrappers for the foodstuffs so that these provide a stimulus for the children to talk about the problems they are trying to solve.

■ Challenge
Allow the children time to choose a recipe card and, with a partner, devise some challenges related to the new recipe that are similar to those they have solved on Resource Sheet 61.

PLENARY

Invite pairs of children to tell the class the method they used in solving one of the challenges on the resource sheet. Discuss alternative methods.

Key fact or strategy
There are 1 000 g in 1 kilogram and 1 000 ml in 1 litre.

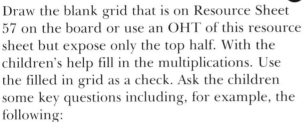

Lesson 3

◣ Learning objectives
Mental/oral starter:
- Recall multiplication facts to 10×10

Main teaching activities:
- Use addition, subtraction, multiplication and division to solve word problems involving time

📖 Resources
Make an OHT of Resource Sheet 57 (If required for use in the mental/oral starter.), photocopies of Resource Sheet 58

ᵃᵇᶜ Vocabulary
Multiplication square, hour, time

MENTAL/ORAL STARTER 🕙

Draw the blank grid that is on Resource Sheet 57 on the board or use an OHT of this resource sheet but expose only the top half. With the children's help fill in the multiplications. Use the filled in grid as a check. Ask the children some key questions including, for example, the following:
Which do you think are the trickiest multiplications?
(examples include 7×8 and 7×9)

Why is there only half a multiplication square here? (the products are replicated on the other half)

MAIN ACTIVITY 🕙

Whole class, individuals, pairs, small groups

Remind the children of the units of time and how to use the 24-hour clock. Give each child a copy of Resource Sheet 58 and time to try the puzzles set in the cake factory. They can record their answers in their workbooks.

■ Support
The children may like to make some rough drawings of Doreen's day or the assembly line for the cakes to help them interpret the problems.

■ Challenge
Ask the children to create more puzzles involving a 5% increase in orders, overtime for Doreen, or a breakdown in production resulting in short-time working (perhaps Doreen works half time).

PLENARY 🕙

Invite individual children to describe how they solved each of the problems.

Key fact or strategy
Time taken is solved by finding the difference between time finished and time begun.

Lesson 4

◣ Learning objectives
Mental/oral starter:
- Convert kg to g and litres to millilitres

Main teaching activities:
- Use mathematical operations to solve time word problems involving timetables

◢ Resources
A list of masses in kilograms and capacities in litres along with an accompanying list saying what the masses and capacities are when converted into grams and millilitres (The list should be prepared on an OHT or written on the board before the lesson. An example list is shown below. If the school is near the sea, a local tide table would be useful.), photocopies of Resource Sheet 59

ᵃᵇᶜ Vocabulary
Kilograms, grams, litres, millilitres, 24-hour, p.m.

MENTAL/ORAL STARTER

Cover the answers on the prepared lists before showing the lists of masses and capacities to the children. Here is an example list.

Masses and capacities

kilograms/litres	gram/milliliters
171 kg	
2 kg	
4 litres	
2.5 litres	
3.25 kg	
4.35 litres	
46.2 kg	
13.75 litres	
76.05 litres	
22.2 kg	

Ask individual children to convert each of the amounts to grams or millilitres. Reveal the answers as you go along. Add new amounts to the list until the children are confident about these conversions.

MAIN ACTIVITY

Whole class, individuals, pairs

Remind the children of how we denote times when using the 24-hour clock. Ask them to convert times to the 24-hour notation, for example, 4 p.m., 10:30 p.m., a quarter past eight in the evening.

Talk to the children about the motion of the tides. Why is it important to produce tide tables for mariners? Give a copy of Resource Sheet 59 to each child. Read it aloud and answer the children's questions about it. Allow the children to work alone to solve the puzzles.

■ Support
Allow the children to support one another by working in pairs or a group to solve the puzzles.

■ Challenge
The children can work out the times between all tides on the chart.

PLENARY

Work through the resource sheet with the children's help so that the children can check their answers.

Key fact or strategy
How to read a timetable by incorporating times in 24-hour clock notation.

Supplementary activities

Mental/oral follow-up

Give the children lists of decimals with one, three or four decimal places, to place in size order.

Invite the children to make conversions from metres to centimetres and kilograms to grams. Use the list given below.

These details of record breaking vegetables, fruits and flowers are taken from past UK national records.

Type	Size
Beetroot	13.49 kg
Carrot	4.65 kg
Dahlia	3.3 m
Gladiolus	2.55 m
Gooseberry	58.5 g
Grapefruit	1.67 kg
Lemon	2.13 kg
Lupin	1.9 m
Melon (cantaloupe)	8.33 kg
Petunia	2.53 m
Pumpkin	322 kg
Sunflower	7.17 m
Tomato	2.56 kg
Tomato plant	13.96 m
Watermelon	16.33 kg

© **Guinness World Records 1992.**

Homework

Ask the children to try inventing a little game or puzzle that involves the cake factory used in Lesson 3. Here are some starter ideas:
- a track game following a journey along the assembly line that has to be completed inside a fixed time, with time loss hazards along the way
- a card game involving collecting time points
- a "Bingo" board that involves setting out times during Doreen's day to match production processes.

Unit 11 **Supplementary activities**

Development

Write this snippet from a railway timetable on the board.

Manchester Piccadilly	14:23	14:30
Stockport	14:33	14:42
Wilmslow		
Chester		
Crewe		
Macclesfield	14:52	14:59
Congleton		15:08
Stoke-on-Trent	15:12	15:20
Stafford		15:44
Wolverhampton		15:59
Birmingham New Street		16:19
Nuneaton		
Rugby		
Milton Keynes Central	16:20	
Watford Junction		
London Euston	17:02	

Discuss how the times are set out, how to read the timetable, and all the kinds of information that one can retrieve from a timetable. These include the time of a train, where trains stop, the wait between trains, where to change trains and how long rail journeys take.

Give every child a copy of Resource Sheet 60 and invite them to solve the problems set there. Devise additional puzzles involving this or other timetables.

ICT ideas

Can Do Maths Year 5/P6 CD3 includes "A family outing", a multi-layered problem-solving activity based around the theme of a family journey to the seaside. There are five destinations on the journey. Each destination generates a problem to be solved involving all four operations. The activity is suitable for one child or pairs working co-operatively.

Unit 12 Money and "real-life" problems

Term				Summer 11	

Framework links

11	5	40–47	Mental calculation strategies (+ and –)	Add several numbers. Use known facts and place value for mental addition and subtraction.
		48–51	Pencil and paper procedures (+ and –)	Extend written methods: addition and subtraction of integers less than 10000, and decimals with up to two decimal places.
		82–85	Money and "real-life" problems	Use all four operations to solve money or "real-life" word problems, including percentages.
		70–75	Making decisions, checking results, including using a calculator	Choose appropriate operations/calculation methods. Explain working. Check using sums/differences of odd or even numbers.

Setting the scene	The children have had no opportunity yet in this year to investigate exchange rates and foreign currency. The first two lessons in this unit give them this chance. The remaining two lessons allow them to solve problems involving percentages.

Starting points	In previous units during the year the children have solved single- and multi-step problems, explained their methods and checked their work in a variety of ways. This unit provides the opportunity to build on the knowledge they have gained and to develop practices with which they are familiar.

Checking progress	■ All the children should know what the exchange rate is and calculate simple exchanges from one currency to another. They should say what a percentage is and be able to tackle problems involving percentages.
	■ Some children will need to be reminded of the need for exchange rates and the process involved in finding a percentage.
	■ Some children should be confident in exchange rate use and will be able to move on to creating additional problems that involve percentages by starting with the data they are given.

Lesson 1

 Learning objectives
Mental/oral starter:
• Put in order decimals with the same number of decimal places
Main teaching activities:
• Use mathematical operations to solve money problems
• Explain how they solved the problems

Resources
Sample coins of different currencies (if these are available), photocopies of Resource Sheet 61

Vocabulary
Digit, decimal, decimal place, exchange rate, buy, currency

MENTAL/ORAL STARTER

Write any four digits on the board (they need not all be different). Invite the children to create as many decimals with two decimal places as they can from the digits. If the digits are: 3544, the resulting decimals will be 35.44, 54.43, 54.34, 44.35, 44.53, 45.35, 45.53, 43.54, 43.45, 34.54, 34.45 and 53.44.

Ask the children to place these in ascending or descending order of size.

Repeat the exercise by using another starter set of four digits.

MAIN ACTIVITY

Whole class, individuals

Pass around the foreign coins so that the children can look at them. Discuss where the children have been on holiday and some of their experiences with foreign currencies. Talk about exchange rates and what they mean. Give each child a copy of Resource Sheet 61. Read aloud the introduction and explain that the chart of exchange rates tells you what you would have for every £1 that you exchange for another currency. Ask the children to try to solve the four problems on the resource sheet.

■ Support

Discuss again the idea of exchange rate with the children. Answer any questions they may have and show them how to tackle the first problem.

■ Challenge

Ask the children to double the amounts of pounds sterling in the puzzles and find out the equivalent in each of the four foreign currencies.

PLENARY

Write the exchange rate chart from Resource Sheet 61 on the board. Ask individual children to calculate what they would obtain by offering different amounts of pounds sterling.

Key fact or strategy
We need mathematical skills to exchange pounds sterling for other currencies.

Lesson 2

Learning objectives
Mental/oral starter:
- Add pairs of two-digit numbers

Main teaching activities:
- Use mathematical operations to solve money problems
- Explain how they solved the problems

Resources
Sample coins of different currencies (if these are available), photocopies of Resource Sheet 62

Vocabulary
Two-digit, add, exchange rate, buy, currency, pounds sterling

MENTAL/ORAL STARTER

Write the school telephone number up on the board. Invite the children to use these digits to make some two-digit numbers. Ask the children to add pairs of the two-digit numbers together and give you the answers.

Use another telephone number chosen at random from the telephone directory. Create a new set of two-digit number pairs for addition.

MAIN ACTIVITY

Whole class, pairs

Remind the children of what an exchange rate is. Tell them that we can exchange pounds sterling for other currencies and we can change the money back. Because of the status of one currency when compared with another, which varies because of banking and other economic activity, exchange of currency may be to our advantage one way but not so the other way.

Hand around a copy of Resource Sheet 62 for each child. Talk it through. Organise the children into pairs. Suggest that one child plays the banker while the other is the customer. Together they can solve the puzzles and write the answers in their books.

■ Support
Invite the children to support one another within a group. Set up a strategy for tackling the first problem with them.

■ Challenge
The children who finish can offer their help to those who are finding the work difficult.

PLENARY

Choose from the resource sheet those problems that the children found difficult. Discuss with them how they might be tackled. Children who have completed the problems can discuss their methods.

Key fact or strategy
Exchange rates involve buying and selling currencies.

Lesson 3

Learning objectives
Mental/oral starter:
• Add pairs of two-digit numbers
Main teaching activities:
• Use addition, subtraction, multiplication and division to solve money and "real-life" problems, involving percentages

Resources
Calculators, photocopies of Resource Sheet 63, data relating to the class (numbers in the class, number of girls, and so on, ready for a challenge in the main activity)

Vocabulary
Two-digit numbers, add, percentage, per cent, %

MENTAL/ORAL STARTER

Write the digits 0, 1, 2, 3, 4, 5, 6, 7, 8, 9 on the board. Organise the children into groups. Ask each group to make three pairs of two-digit numbers that sum to a total less than 100 and three pairs that sum to a total greater that 100. (Remind them that they can use any digit as often as they like.)

Take a pair of numbers from each group and ask the whole class to calculate the answer. Go around the groups again for the next pair of numbers. Continue until it is time to begin the main activity.

MAIN ACTIVITY

Whole class, individuals

Ask the children what they understand by a *percentage*. Explain that *per cent* means *for every hundred* and a percentage tells us the number of parts in every hundred.

Write up 50%, 25%, 10% and other common percentages on the board. Discuss these with the children.

Hand each child a copy of Resource Sheet 63. Ask the children to attempt the "Percentage challenge".

■ Support

Remind the children that *per cent* means *for every hundred*, that is, 50% refers to 50 of every hundred parts. If we can find one hundredth of our total, other percentages can be computed from that. Offer support to individual children in interpreting questions, if they need it.

■ Challenge

Give the children some data relating to the class. This could include the following:

• number of children in the class
• number of boys
• number having a packed lunch
• number having birthdays in November (or the autumn term)
• number who know their 7 times table.

Based on these data, the children can use a calculator to work out some percentages.

PLENARY

Either check through the problems on Resource Sheet 63 and invite the children to make calculator checks of the answers or take the challenge data from above and ask the children to predict what the percentages of the whole class will be. Invite the children who have tackled these problems to say what the percentages are. Discuss the mismatches between prediction and actual figures, for example, close to 50% of the class should be boys.

Key fact or strategy
A percentage is the number of parts in a hundred. Percentages are important to understand as we use them in everyday life.

Lesson 4

✎ **Learning objectives**

Mental/oral starter:
- Subtract pairs of two-digit numbers

Main teaching activities:
- Use addition, subtraction, multiplication and division to solve money and "real-life" problems, involving percentages

📖 **Resources**
Photocopies of Resource Sheet 64, calculators, a pound coin (for Support)

🔤 **Vocabulary**
Two-digit, subtract, percentage, per cent, %

MENTAL/ORAL STARTER

Write on the board some two-digit subtractions that are interesting to discuss. Here are some suggestions.

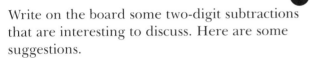

89 – 39	76 – 67	32 – 11
48 – 25	99 – 88	51 – 24

Ask the children to work out the first subtraction. Discuss all the ways they used to work it out. Individual children may say some of the following:

- I saw they both had nine and so I just subtracted 30 from 80.

- I rounded the numbers to 90 and 40 and as I had rounded both by adding 1, I got the answer straightaway.

- I rounded 89 to 90 and took 39 away from that. Then I took one away from the answer I got.

Write up the next pair of numbers from the list and discuss how the answer can be achieved here. Work down the list in the same way.

MAIN ACTIVITY

Pairs, whole class

In pairs, allow the children to attempt the problems on Resource Sheet 64. When the first pair complete them all, bring the class together and work through the problems that every child has completed. Pass around calculators so that the children can use these to do another check on their work so far. Collect in the calculators. Ask the children to continue the resource sheet

work. Those children who have finished can complete the challenge below.

■ Support

Remind the children of what we mean by percentage and look together at simple percentages like 50%. Take a £1 coin from your pocket and, with appropriate questioning, establish what simple percentages of a pound are in pence. Show the children how this can be worked out arithmetically. Set them going on the next problem on the resource sheet.

■ Challenge

Ask the children to draw on a piece of paper four stationery items that they would like to sell. They should then give each a wholesale price and work out what the selling price would be with 2%, 5%, 10% and 25% profit.

PLENARY

Discuss methods used in the rest of the work on Resource Sheet 64. Allow those children who needed support to make the checks on the calculators. Ask children who began the stationery challenge to show their work and talk about it.

Key fact or strategy
A percentage is the number of parts in a hundred. Percentages are important to understand as we use them in everyday life.

Supplementary activities

Mental/oral follow-up

Ask the children to recall the date of their birthday. The digits from this can be used to generate an array of two-digit numbers, which can be added to and subtracted from one another in pairs.

Homework

The children can complete or begin the challenge given to some of them in the lesson. They should draw four stationery items that they would like to sell. They should then give each a wholesale price and work out what the selling price would be with 2%, 5%, 10% and 25% profit.

Development

Collect junk mail information relating to sales in the shops. Look for "percentage off" offers. Use these to create a percentage workshop for the children.

Look for the possibility of using percentages related to scores in the children's favourite sports, for example, how often does the player who takes the conversions convert tries into goals in rugby matches? Is it more than 95% of the time? If information is available about the school football or netball teams, percentages can be calculated relating to home and away matches.

ICT ideas

Lifeskills Time and Money (Learning and Teaching Scotland) offers a range of stimulating activities set within a townscape where children are encouraged to learn by solving puzzles and managing everyday situations. The teacher can customise the content of this package to meet the needs of individual ability levels.

Unit 12 **Supplementary activities**

Camp provisions

Baked beans
4 tins £1.39

Marmalade
86p

Washing-up
liquid 79p

Ketchup
£0.69

Spaghetti
72p

Margarine
£0.37

Rice £1.09

Bacon £1.69

Sunflower oil 49p

Drinking
chocolate 95p

Cornflakes
£0.90

6 eggs £1.09

Large loaf 44p

Biscuits 69p

Pan scourer
36p

Potatoes
£2.29 for 5 kg

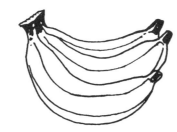

Bananas
50p for $\frac{1}{2}$ kg

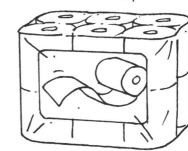

Toilet rolls
£3.49 per pack

Resource sheet 1

Going to camp

Gail is buying things for camp.

1 Which of these pairs of items could she buy for less than £3? Estimate first.

   a) Drinking chocolate and 6 eggs
   b) Bacon and a pan scourer
   c) Potatoes and biscuits
   d) Baked beans and ketchup

2 If these items were half price in the shop, what would Gail pay for each?

   a) Pan scourer
   b) Cornflakes
   c) Large loaf

3 What would Gail pay for 2 of each of these items? Check your answers by estimating.

   a) Jar of marmalade
   b) Tub of margarine
   c) Bottle of sunflower oil
   d) Bag of potatoes

4 What is the difference in price between these pairs of items?

   a) Toilet rolls and potatoes
   b) Bacon and cornflakes
   c) Rice and ketchup

Maths Action Plans, Problems and Data Year 5/P6 © David Clemson and Wendy Clemson, Nelson Thornes Ltd, 2002

Shopping lists

Gail and John have written their own shopping lists.

> 8 tins baked beans
> 10 kg potatoes
> 2 boxes corrnflakes
> 1 dozen eggs
> 3 loaves
> 1 bottle ketchup
> 1 pack bacon
> 1 bottle sunflower oil

> 10 kg potatoes
> 6 packs biscuits
> 2 jars drinking chocolate
> 4 tins Baked beans

I should be able to buy this lot for about £15.

Gail

This won't cost me more than £10.

John

---

1 Check it out! Are both Gail and John correct?
Try estimating to confirm your answers.

---

2 If there are 16 people going to camp, can you find out the cost of 16 of each of these items?

Hint: Try multiplying by 8 and then doubling your answers.

1 banana	18p
4 slices bread	8p
a portion of spaghetti	9.5p
3 biscuits	15p

Maths Action Plans, Problems and Data Year 5/P6 © David Clemson and Wendy Clemson, Nelson Thornes Ltd, 2002

Travelling to camp

1 There are 43 people going to camp in total.
Each minibus holds 15 people.
How many seats will be empty?

2 Of the people travelling to camp, 23 live in Woodbury, a quarter of the rest live in Leafley and a fifth live in Plantpool. The rest live in Budley.

How many people live in:

a) Leafley?

b) Plantpool?

c) Budley?

3 The minibus charge is £39 per bus.
If every person pays £3.50, how much will be left over for camp funds?

4 The 29 children at camp each have £5 pocket money.
How much money is that in total?

Explain how you did the calculations and make estimates to check your answer.

Maths Action Plans, Problems and Data Year 5/P6 © David Clemson and Wendy Clemson, Nelson Thornes Ltd, 2002

Number ladders

21	71	63	88
46	14	43	93
32	36	82	37
95	48	11	68
62	86	92	59
91	16	64	45
25	52	22	74
39	76	50	41
80	28	19	33
54	44	34	20
79	90	44	96
27	56	75	53
99	38	42	57

Resource sheet 5

How likely ... ? (1)

How likely is each of these events?

I will be older next year.

I will meet King Henry VIII on my way home.

I will travel in outer space one day.

I will play football for my favourite team.

I will see the headteacher this week.

How likely … ? (2)

Talk about these events. How likely are they?

Tomorrow will be Sunday.

A kite can be made to fly if the string is long enough.

It will rain tomorrow.

If I toss a coin three times, I will get three heads.

At least one person in my class was born in the same month as me.

If I roll a dice, the number I get is an even number.

If I roll a dice, the number I get will be greater than zero.

There is a monster in Loch Ness.

Resource sheet 7

Maths Action Plans, Problems and Data Year 5/P6 © David Clemson and Wendy Clemson, Nelson Thornes Ltd, 2002

Likelihood scales

Here is a "likelihood scale"!

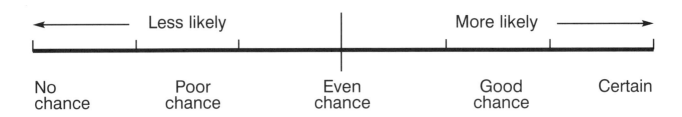

← Less likely	More likely →
No chance	Poor chance	Even chance	Good chance	Certain

Look at each of the events below. Decide where you think each one fits along the scale and write in its number. For example, if you think there is a poor chance that all brown haired people are good at dancing, write 1 under "poor chance" on the likelihood scale.

---

1 All brown haired people are good at dancing.

---

2 It will snow this afternoon.

---

3 My birthday will be the same date next year.

---

4 Everyone in school always works harder on Fridays.

5 In a bag of jelly sweets there will be at least one red one.

Maths Action Plans, Problems and Data Year 5/P6 © David Clemson and Wendy Clemson, Nelson Thornes Ltd, 2002

Frequency diagrams

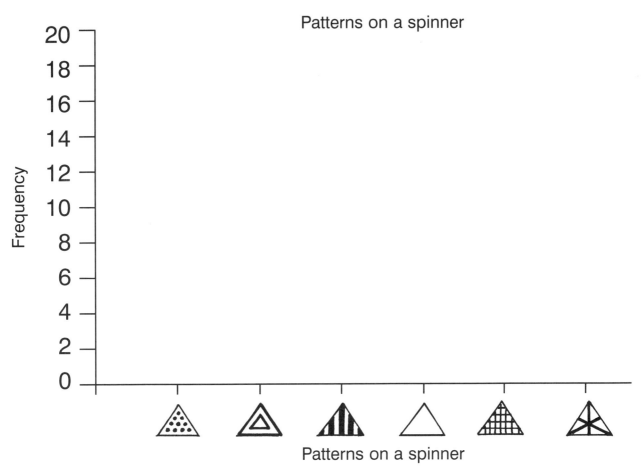

Patterns on a spinner

Patterns on a spinner

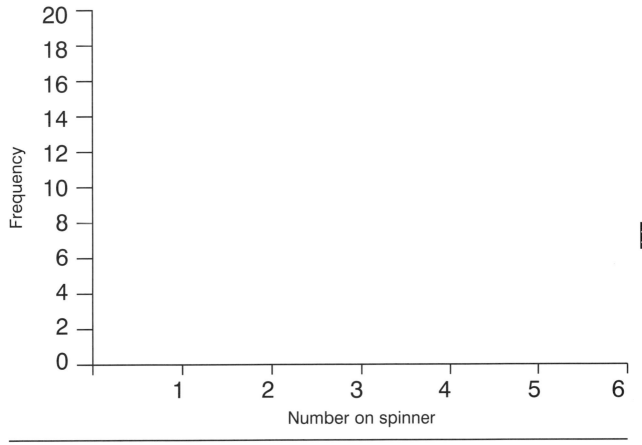

Numbers on a spinner

Maths Action Plans, Problems and Data Year 5/P6 © David Clemson and Wendy Clemson, Nelson Thornes Ltd, 2002

Temperature charts

Meteorologists in Townsville did an experiment. They wrote down a list of temperatures and then calculated how many days in the year the temperature in Townsville had peaked at these figures.

Here are the results:

Test temperature	0°C	12°C	17°C	23°C	29°C
Number of days	20	35	40	15	10

Put these figures into the chart below to make a bar line chart.

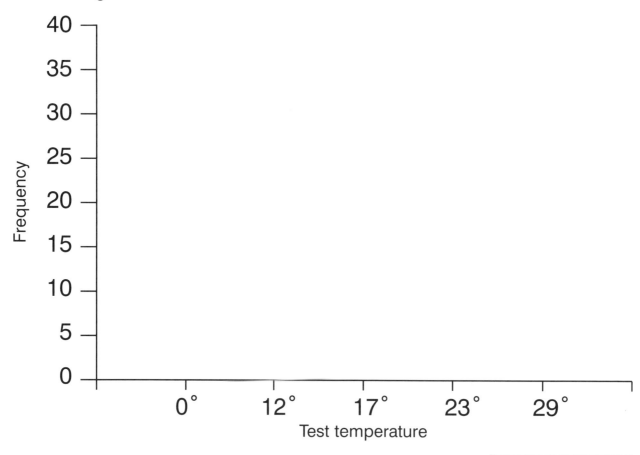

1 Which test temperature was most often the peak?

2 On how many days was the peak 12°C?

3 When in the year would you expect the number of days with a temperature of 29°C to fall?

4 How many days' temperatures featured in the experiment?

Maths Action Plans, Problems and Data Year 5/P6 © David Clemson and Wendy Clemson, Nelson Thornes Ltd, 2002

Jelly beans test

Some bags of jelly beans were opened by Alison. She counted how many green jelly beans were in each bag. There was at least one in every bag. Here is the bar line chart that she made.

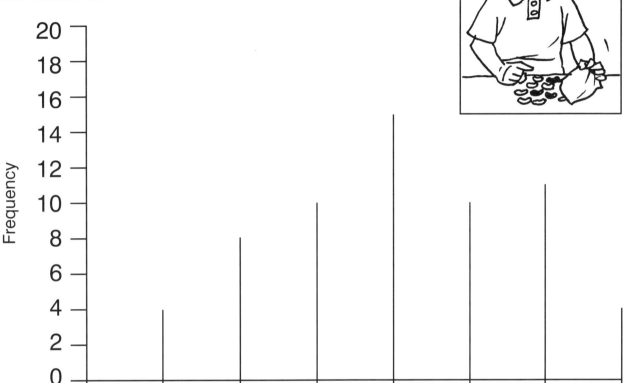

1   How many bags had 4 green jelly beans in them?

2   How many bags had more than 6 green jelly beans in them?

3   How many bags did Alison open in total?

4   If you had a similar bag of jelly beans, how many green jelly beans do you think would be most likely in your bag?

5   How many bags had fewest green jelly beans in them?

Maths Action Plans, Problems and Data Year 5/P6 © David Clemson and Wendy Clemson, Nelson Thornes Ltd, 2002

Standing room only!

Different numbers of passengers take the Number 16 bus from the station to the shops each day.

The bus is always full but the number of standing passengers varies.

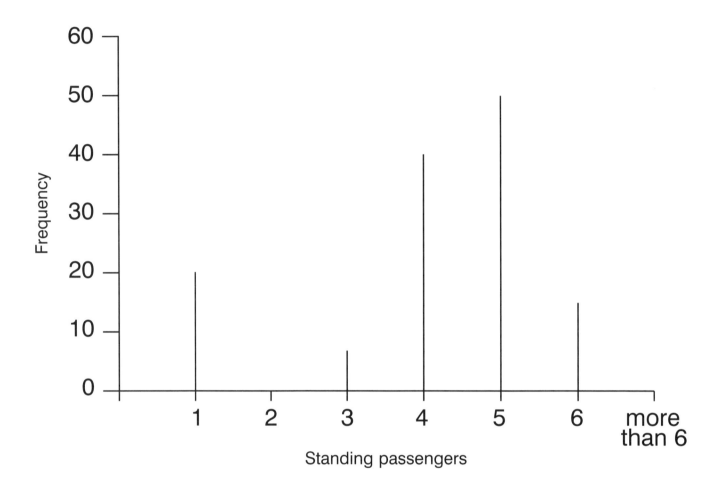

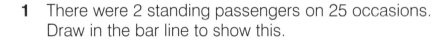

1 There were 2 standing passengers on 25 occasions.
Draw in the bar line to show this.

2 The bus company will put in more seats to match the most common numbers of passengers.
How many is that?

3 On how many trips did the bus carry 1, 2 or 3 standing passengers?

Maths Action Plans, Problems and Data Year 5/P6 © David Clemson and Wendy Clemson, Nelson Thornes Ltd, 2002

Checkout data

At the speedy checkout in the supermarket, the manager decides to check how often customers buy only 1 to 10 items. Here is his data.

Number of items	Number of times bought	Number of items	Number of times bought
1	30	6	100
2	45	7	90
3	15	8	85
4	60	9	60
— 5	70	10	90

1 Draw a bar line chart to show this data. Remember to label the axes and give your chart a title.

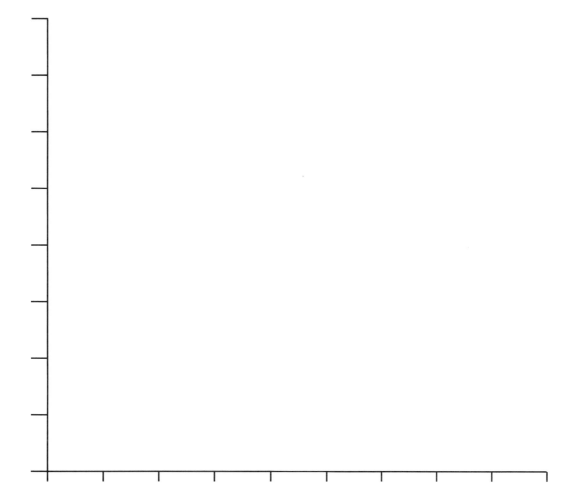

2 Invent four questions that can be answered by looking at your chart. Ask a classmate to answer them.

Panto audiences

Use the panto audience information to create a bar line graph.
Your Y axis scale should be in hundreds.

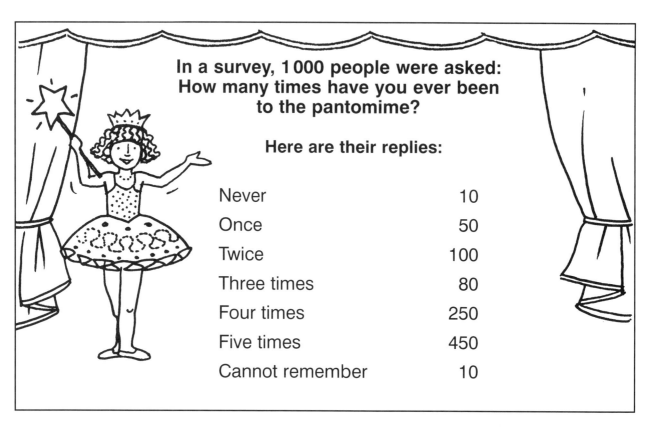

**In a survey, 1000 people were asked:
How many times have you ever been
to the pantomime?**

Here are their replies:

Never	10
Once	50
Twice	100
Three times	80
Four times	250
Five times	450
Cannot remember	10

When your chart is complete answer these questions.

1 How many people have been more than three times?

2 How many people have been less than twice?

3 Does the data show that panto is popular?
Explain your answer.

4 Would it be worth finding out whether people have been more than five times? Explain your answer.

Resource sheet 14

Cat food

"Most cat owners prefer to give their cats Cattodins."

Is this true?

	Cattodins	Pussygrub
Alan		
Bryony		
Corinne		
Darren		
Iqbal		
Fiona		
Sumi		
Heather		
Isobel		
Jack		

1 What is the mode for Cattodins?

2 What is the range for Cattodins?

3 What is the mode for Pussygrub?

4 What is the range for Pussygrub?

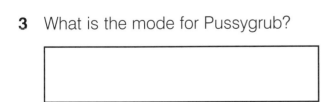

Paper sizes

This worksheet is printed on a piece of paper called size A4. But what is "A4"? Find out the size of A4 and other paper sizes by using the diagram below.

A0 (A zero) is the size of paper from which all other sizes are worked out. A0 is a rectangle with an area of 1 square metre and sides measuring 1 189 mm and 841 mm. A1 is half that size, A2 half the size of A1, and so on.

Work out the paper sizes in the chart below, rounding down to the nearest mm where necessary.

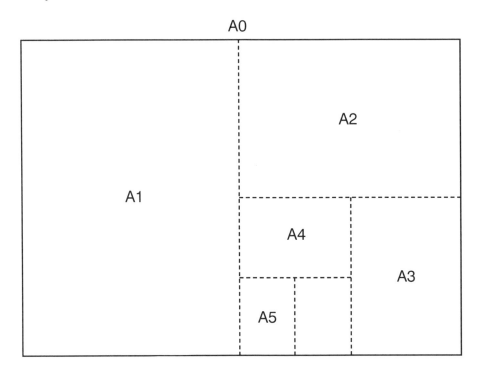

Size	Measurements (mm)
A0	1 189 × 841
A1	
A2	
A3	
A4	
A5	

Distances

A Solve the journey problems below by using the kilometres chart.

Distance in kilometres

London

328	Manchester		
1782	2126	Oslo	
420	764	1791	Paris
1812	2156	2591	1418	Rome

1 Claud is driving with his family from Paris to Rome. How far is that?

2 Is it further from London to Oslo or London to Rome? What is the difference between these two distances?

3 How much further is it from Rome to Manchester than Paris to London?

B Bob is a fencing expert. He has fencing panels 1 m, 1.5 m and 2.5 m long.

1 What would be the combination of panels that would exactly cover these distances?

2 m

3.5 m

27 m

12 m

2 Are there other combinations of panels that would exactly cover these distances?

3 If Bob needs seven 1 m panels and five 2.5 m panels how long a fence is he making?

Maths Action Plans, Problems and Data Year 5/P6 © David Clemson and Wendy Clemson, Nelson Thornes Ltd, 2002

Resource sheet 17

Fun Park

Solve the problems based on the Fun Park rides.

1 The Park opens an hour after sunrise and closes two hours before sunset. If sunrise is 07:15 and sunset is at 8:50 in the evening, for how long is Fun Park open?

3 Someone goes through the turnstile into the Fun Park every 4 seconds. How many people pass through in:

1 minute

12 minutes

½ hour

5 The kiddy ride has an automatic stop button after 3 minutes. If the ride begins at these times, when does it stop?

12:51

13:59

14:00

15:57

17:09

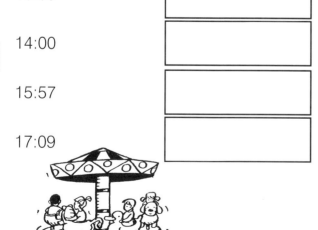

2 The pony and trap takes 27 minutes to go round the Fun Park, with five-minute breaks between rides. If the pony begins work at 10:30 and goes round 6 times, when will he finish?

4 How many horse race games lasting 12 minutes each can be fitted into an hour?

6 Fun Park has a moving robot. When a coin is put into a slot he moves for 23.5 seconds. For how long will he move if these numbers of coins are put into him?

5 coins

3 coins

10 coins

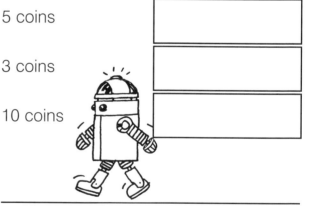

7 A pinball game takes Sanjay 36.2 seconds to play, Ching 45.7 seconds and Jenny 34.3 seconds. How long in total did the games take?

Maths Action Plans, Problems and Data Year 5/P6 © David Clemson and Wendy Clemson, Nelson Thornes Ltd, 2002

Start time, stop time

How long does it take?

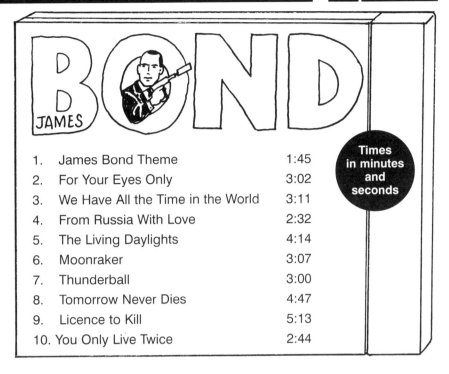

1.	James Bond Theme	1:45
2.	For Your Eyes Only	3:02
3.	We Have All the Time in the World	3:11
4.	From Russia With Love	2:32
5.	The Living Daylights	4:14
6.	Moonraker	3:07
7.	Thunderball	3:00
8.	Tomorrow Never Dies	4:47
9.	Licence to Kill	5:13
10.	You Only Live Twice	2:44

Times in minutes and seconds

Here are the playing times for some of the music from James Bond movies in minutes and seconds. Can you solve these timing puzzles?

1 How long do tracks 1 and 4 play for in total?

2 What is the total time taken for:

tracks 3 and 5?

tracks 7, 9 and 10?

all tracks?

3 If tracks 2 and 3 are played twice each, how long will this take?

4 How long would it take to play track 7 four times?

5 What is the difference in playing time between:

tracks 2 and 6?

tracks 1 and 3 and 8 and 10?

the longest and shortest tracks?

Ultimate challenge

If the CD is listened to in 3 minute episodes, write down which tracks will be playing as each 3 minutes is up.

Resource sheet 19

Summer garden fun

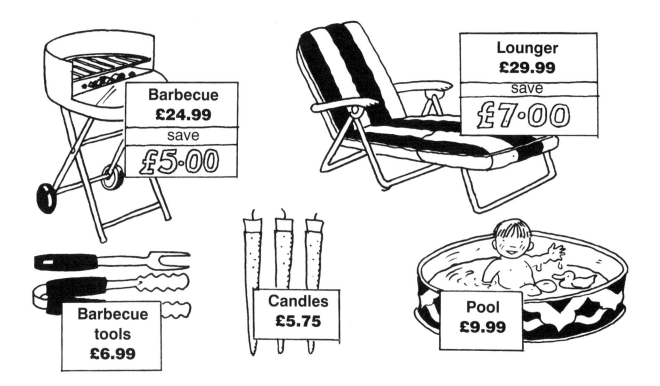

Barbecue
£24.99
save
£5·00

Lounger
£29.99
save
£7·00

Barbecue tools
£6.99

Candles
£5.75

Pool
£9.99

Use the prices of the garden items to solve the challenges below.

1 What was the original price of the barbecue?

2 What was the original price of the lounger?

3 What is the difference in price between:

the pool and the candles?

the barbecue and the barbecue tools?

4 What change would you get from a £20 note …

if you bought a pool?

if you bought barbecue tools?

5 What would four packs of candles cost?

6 Approximately how much does each of the barbecue tools in the set cost?

Puzzles

Use adding, subtracting, multiplying and dividing to solve these puzzles.

Think of a number!

− 46 answer 17 ~ my number is?

× 17 answer 425 ~ my number is?

÷ 30 answer 50 ~ my number is?

1

beanbag
ball

triceratops

mini
magnet

These are gifts given away with children's meals in "Quickie Meal" burger house. Here are the numbers taken in some stores. Find the totals.

   119 + 58
350 + 147

     256 + 99
509 + 213

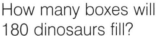   711 + 308
438 + 384

2

Dinosaurs are in collections − 12 in a box. How many would we find in:

4 boxes?

9 boxes?

13 boxes?

How many boxes will 180 dinosaurs fill?

3
The "Quickie Meal" burger house has seats for 85

and 27.

How many people can be seated altogether?

If there are 46 people in the restaurant, how many more can get a seat?

Maths Action Plans, Problems and Data Year 5/P6 © David Clemson and Wendy Clemson, Nelson Thornes Ltd, 2002

Resource sheet 21

Pocket and holiday money

A How much is saved by these children in a year?

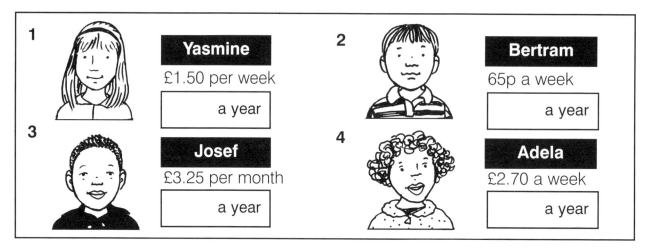

1
Yasmine
£1.50 per week

a year

2
Bertram
65p a week

a year

3
Josef
£3.25 per month

a year

4
Adela
£2.70 a week

a year

B As well as their pocket money, the children have holiday money.

Yasmine

1 Yasmin does a paper round to earn £15.50 a month. How much is that in a year?

Bertram

2 Bertram has £2 each from 4 uncles and 7 cousins. How much is that in total?

Josef

3 Josef helps Grandad in his garden. Grandad gives him £3.50, £17.20 and £6.25 during the year. How much is that in total?

Adela

4 Adela gets 50p a week from Auntie and £10 on her birthday. How much is that in a year?

Maths Action Plans, Problems and Data Year 5/P6 © David Clemson and Wendy Clemson, Nelson Thornes Ltd, 2002

Number square

Write out the calculation you do to reach the answer.

20	30	40	50	60	70	80
21	31	41	51	61	71	81
22	32	42	52	62	72	82
23	33	43	53	63	73	83
24	34	44	54	64	74	84
25	35	45	55	65	75	85
26	36	46	56	66	76	86
27	37	47	57	67	77	87
28	38	48	58	68	78	88
29	39	49	59	69	79	89

Resource sheet 23

Stamps and coins

1 Malik has been finding out the fewest number of coins that make 1p, 2p, 3p … up to 20p.

He says that only 18p and 19p need as many as 4 coins. The rest can all be made with fewer than 4 coins. Is he right?

2 If you had three 28p stamps and three 26p stamps, find out all the postage amounts that you could make.

3 These envelopes all need stamps. How could you buy the stamps by using these numbers of coins? What coins would you use?

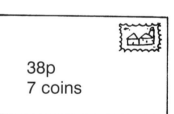

38p
7 coins

£1.10
3 coins or 11 coins

56p
3 coins or 6 coins

27p
4 coins

Resource sheet 24

Add to 1000

50 + 950

100 + 900

150 + 850

200 + 800

250 + 750

300 + 700

350 + 650

400 + 600

450 + 550

500 + 500

The school stock cupboard

5015 sheets of blue paper

7 shelves of text books

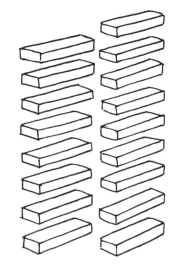

17 packs with 144 pencils in each

1 If one fifth of the blue paper is used how many sheets are left?

What is half of the remaining sheets?

2 On the seven shelves of textbooks there are 1202 books.
Three shelves have 150 books on each of them.
The other four shelves all have the same number of books on each.
How many books does each of these four shelves hold?

3 How many pencils are there in half a pack?

How many pencils are there in 10 packs?

If 8 packs of pencils are used, how many pencils remain in the stock cupboard?

Rosemary's garden centre

See if you can solve the garden centre challenges.

1

Seedlings come in pods of 18 plants.

What is a half of this number?

What is one third of the number that are left?

2

The Garden Encyclopaedia reaches the letter Q three fifths of the way through, on page 258. How many pages are there altogether?

3

There are 640 seeds in a pack. By 4 weeks after planting, 192 have come up. How many more must grow to achieve 50% germination?

4

Pansies are popular. At the garden centre, 30 more plants were sold on Thursday than on Wednesday. For both days the total sales were 94. How many were sold on Wednesday?

5

Half the conifers are sold in February. One quarter of those left are sold in March – 23 trees.
How many trees were there in the garden centre at the beginning of February?

Maths Action Plans, Problems and Data Year 5/P6 © David Clemson and Wendy Clemson, Nelson Thornes Ltd, 2002

Resource sheet 27

Pasta feast

Pasta shapes
1 000 g

Tomato paste 200 g

Onion 120 g

Parmesan cheese 80 g

Mushroom
sauce
520 g

Bacon 8 rashers 300 g

Use the pasta feast foods to solve the problems below.

1 A recipe needs half an onion.
What will that weigh?

2 You need 5 g of tomato paste for
every 15 g of onion. How much
tomato paste would you need for:

45 g onion?

105 g onion?

3 If half the mushroom sauce is used,
how much is left?

The whole jar of sauce give 5
servings. How much sauce does
each person eat?

4 In the recipe, 80 g pasta makes
1 serving. How much would you
need for:

4 people?

7 people?

How many portions are there in a
whole pack of pasta shapes?

5 What is the weight of 2 rashers of
bacon?

6 How many jars of mushroom sauce
would we need if we use all the
pasta shapes? Use the answers to
questions 3 and 4 to help you.

7 Mum uses three quarters of the
Parmesan cheese.
How much will be left?

Recipes

Here are the ingredients for foods for a vegetarian picnic.
Use them to solve the puzzles below.

Country pasties

Onion, carrot, potato mix 225 g
Cheese 100 g
Oil 10 ml
Salt and pepper
Wholemeal pastry 425 g

Watercress and carrot salad

Water cress 1 bunch
Carrots 240 g
French dressing 45 ml

Apple swirl

Apples 450 g
Butter 25 g
Brown sugar 50 g
Yoghurt 284 ml

---

1 The recipe makes 4 pasties.

How much pastry would be needed for 10 pasties?

How many pasties would 900 g onion, carrot and potato mix make?

How much cheese would be needed for 14 pasties?

---

2 If one person eats one sixth of the carrots meant for the salad, how much carrot is left?

If the salad recipe feeds 5 how much dressing is needed for 15 people?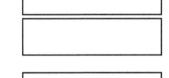

---

3 We need to double the apple swirl recipe for the picnic. Write out the ingredients list.

For this picnic, 1.5 kg apples were bought.
If the double quantity recipe is made up what is the mass of the apples left over?

Mary's pot plant

The growth of Mary's pot plant

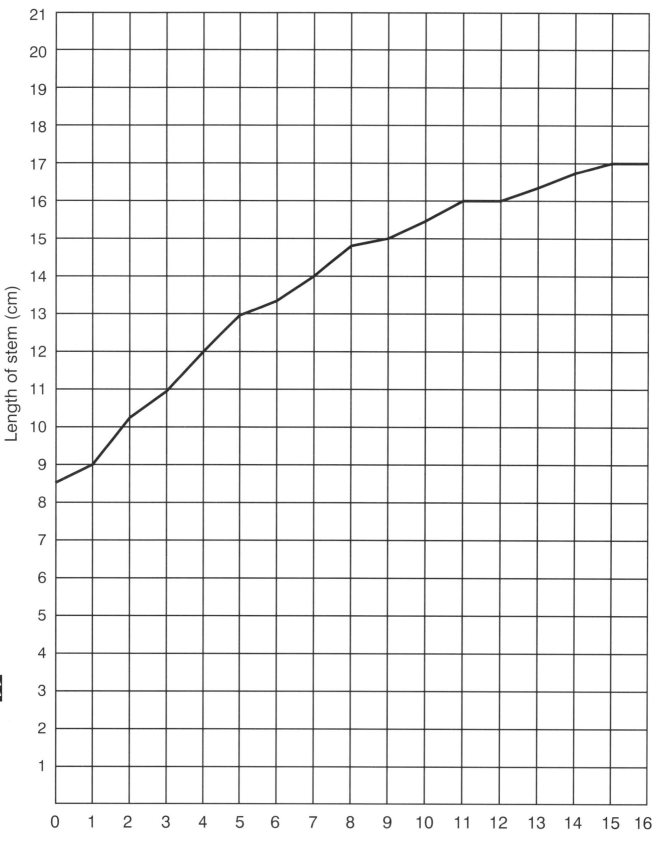

Height chart

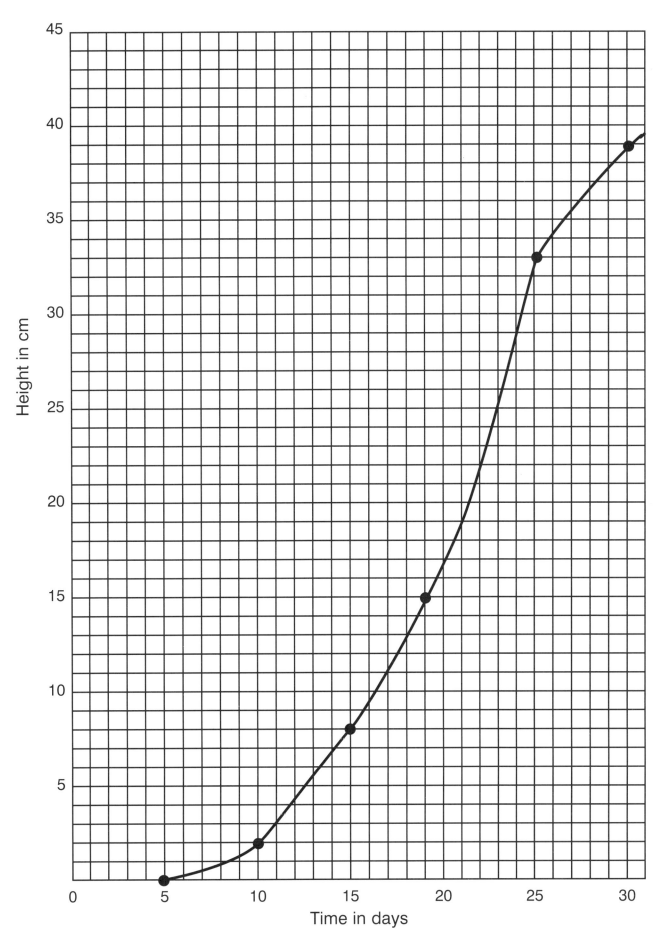

Height in cm

Time in days

Resource sheet 31

Depth chart

A scientist is checking how deep a stream is over 24 hours.
He takes a reading every 2 hours. Here are his results.
Answer the questions about the graph.

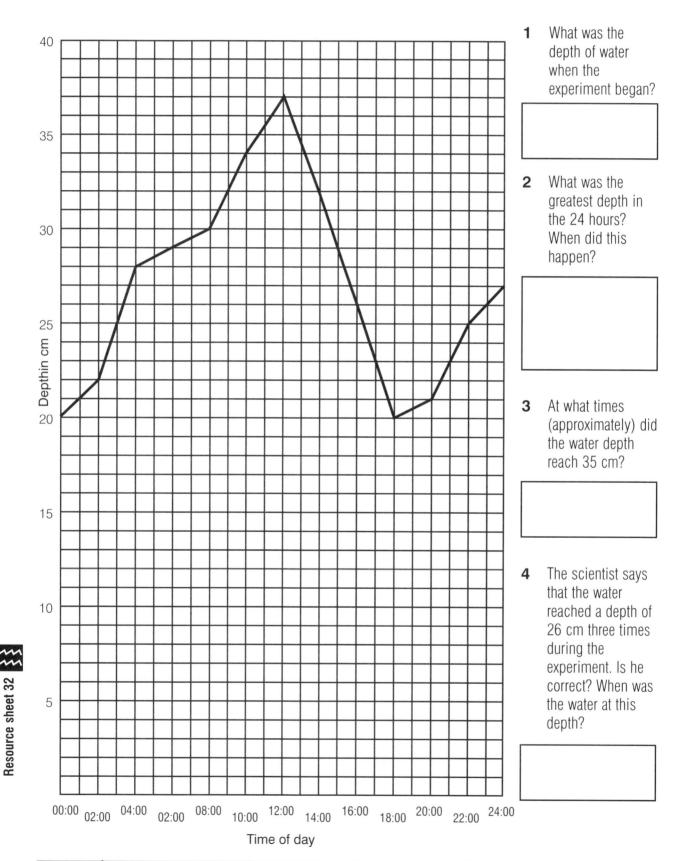

1 What was the depth of water when the experiment began?

2 What was the greatest depth in the 24 hours? When did this happen?

3 At what times (approximately) did the water depth reach 35 cm?

4 The scientist says that the water reached a depth of 26 cm three times during the experiment. Is he correct? When was the water at this depth?

Maths Action Plans, Problems and Data Year 5/P6 © David Clemson and Wendy Clemson, Nelson Thornes Ltd, 2002

Daytime temperatures

These are the daytime temperatures in Chicago for the month of July.

Date	Temperature	Date	Temperature
1	**19**	16	**28**
2	**20**	17	**27**
3	**20**	18	**29**
4	**22**	19	**30**
5	**24**	20	**30**
6	**23**	21	**28**
7	**23**	22	**29**
8	**25**	23	**29**
9	**22**	24	**29**
10	**24**	25	**27**
11	**25**	26	**25**
12	**25**	27	**23**
13	**26**	28	**21**
14	**27**	29	**19**
15	**28**	30	**20**
		31	**20**

Resource sheet 33

Sensor data

Name	Date
Location of sensor	

Time reading taken	Temperature °C	Time reading taken	Temperature °C

Maths Action Plans, Problems and Data Year 5/P6 © David Clemson and Wendy Clemson, Nelson Thornes Ltd, 2002

Number grid

47	82	38	26
22	66	37	70
69	41	34	54
51	96	33	29
84	99	18	58
9	52	72	98
57	2	90	49
43	74	6	85
28	77	31	65
93	64	32	79
48	14	88	40
89	19	11	91
46	68	86	17

Maths Action Plans, Problems and Data Year 5/P6 © David Clemson and Wendy Clemson, Nelson Thornes Ltd, 2002

Number puzzle book

How many pages in a book ...

2 x as long as this? [ ]

3 x as long as this? [ ]

Think of a number puzzle book

by :

I bought three toys all at the same price. I had 76p change from £10.

Which did each toy cost?

[ ]

I threw a dice three times.

The numbers that came up totalled 11.

What numbers could I have thrown?

[ ]

Maths Action Plans, Problems and Data Year 5/P6 © David Clemson and Wendy Clemson, Nelson Thornes Ltd, 2002

More number puzzle pages

Put these numbers in order. What are the missing numbers?

27   33   3

13   21

25   31

1   9   35

15   19   7

[ ]

Think of a number.

Double it.

Add 10.

Subtract 2.

Halve it.

Take away your number …

The answer is 4, isn't it?

Try another number.

I took away 16 and then halved the answer to get 7.

What was my starting number?

[ ]

What is the smallest number divisible by 2, 3, 4, 5, 6 *and* 10?

[ ]

Maths Action Plans, Problems and Data Year 5/P6 © David Clemson and Wendy Clemson, Nelson Thornes Ltd, 2002

Resource sheet 37

Village sports day

Solve the story and money puzzles in your workbook.

1

Angus managed to get 73 people to sponsor him to enter the obstacle race. Each sponsor is giving him 25p. How much should he collect after the race?

If he gets a rosette, the sponsors will give him an extra 20p. How much will he collect if he wins?

2

The raffle is popular. Tickets are 50p or 3 for £1. On sports day, 750 tickets were sold, 120 as "singles". How many were sold in 3s?

What were the takings on single tickets?

... and on 3s?

3

There were 79 entries in the best pot plant contest, 52 in the best cake and 27 in the homemade sweets competition. Entry tickets were 75p. What were the takings?

If prizes cost £13.50 what was the balance?

The entries were all sold and made another £50.92. How much was taken, in total, at the end of the day?

4
Sales in the tea tent

~~~~~~~~~~~~~~~~~~~~

402 glasses of squash
112 lemon ice lollies
179 orange ice lollies

~~~~~~~~~~~~~~~~~~~~

504 cups of tea
376 cups of coffee
213 slices of cake
114 buns

~~~~~~~~~~~~~~~~~~~~

What are these totals? (+ or −)
squash + lemon ice lollies
tea + coffee
cake + buns
tea − cake
total ice lollies
coffee − buns
orange − lemon ice lollies
squash − all ice lollies

Maths Action Plans, Problems and Data Year 5/P6 © David Clemson and Wendy Clemson, Nelson Thornes Ltd, 2002

Bookworm

Join in the Bookworm book sale. Work out which are the best bargains!

1 Novels are £4.99. There are two titles that I really like. Is it worth looking for a third if they are

3 for £10

2 *Explore Space* and *Nature Diary* are

50% off

What are their new prices?

3 If I buy *Explore Space, Nature Diary* and *The Age of Steam*, what do I pay?
What would be the change from £15?
What would I pay if the offer was: Buy 3 get the cheapest free ?

4 In one week the shop sells the following:

Animals	52 copies
Explore Space	18 copies
Teen Pops	115 copies
Nature Diary	46 copies
The Age of Steam	6 copies

All are at full price. What are the shop's takings on each title?

5 If I had £20 to spend what combination of titles could I spend nearly all the money on?

On which titles do they make most money?

6 What would the prices of the books be if all were
10% off?

... the least money?

Maths Action Plans, Problems and Data Year 5/P6 © David Clemson and Wendy Clemson, Nelson Thornes Ltd, 2002

Resource sheet 39

Folding number cards

RESOURCE
SHEET **40**

Cut out each four-part number card.
Fold it up. The last one is blank so that
more can be made and copied.

fold

84	26	17	34
42	13	8.5	17
21	6.5	4.25	8.5

96	46	14	72
48	23	7	36
24	11.5	3.5	18

56	64	69	
28	32	34.5	
14	16	17.25	

Resource sheet 40

Tally chart

Name _____

Maths Action Plans, Problems and Data Year 5/P6 © David Clemson and Wendy Clemson, Nelson Thornes Ltd, 2002

117

Swimming club

Use the information booklet about the swimming club to solve the problems below.

1 How many times do you need to swim in 6 months to make a season ticket worth buying?
If you are aged 45? ... 11? ... 82?

2 What would it cost for 2 adults and 2 children to join the club and pay for one Tuesday swim?

3 How much in 20p coins do you need to pay for 7 lockers? ... 17 lockers?

4 When the lockers are emptied of money, there is £132.80 in them. How many people used a locker?

5 Shamila goes swimming on a Friday. What does it cost for a swim, a locker, a drink and 2 packets of crisps?

6 The Newsons want to join, buy one season ticket and swim. It is Saturday. There are Alun and Maria (Dad and Mum), Jane and Bobby (their children) and Great Gran Agnes (aged 76). What's the total the Newsons must pay?

Maths Action Plans, Problems and Data Year 5/P6 © David Clemson and Wendy Clemson, Nelson Thornes Ltd, 2002

The Swim Locker

THE SWIM LOCKER

SWIM GEAR AT AFFORDABLE PRICES

Girls' and women's costumes

All the latest swim goggles

Trunks

Swim hats in all sizes

Floats and water wings

Swim shorts

Swim towels

Match attendances

Here are the numbers of spectators at seven matches at Hightown Rovers' home ground.

Match 1	1800	Match 2	2600	Match 3	950
Match 4	1550	Match 5	2100	Match 6	1750
Match 7	2350				

1 Make a bar line chart below to show this information.

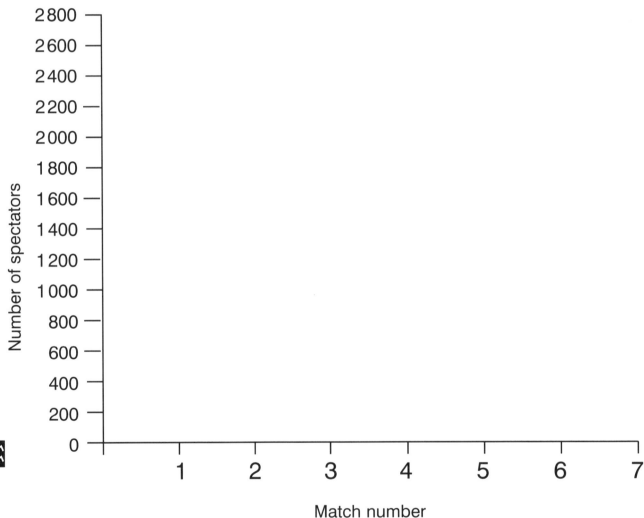

2 On rough paper or in your notebook, write down four questions that can be answered by looking at the chart. Ask a classmate to answer them.

Growth chart

The pygmy shrew is the smallest British mammal.
When full grown its body is only 6.5 cm long.

A baby pygmy shrew was measured at 2 week intervals.
Here are the measurements:

Just born	0.8 cm	2 weeks	1.7 cm	4 weeks	2.6 cm
6 weeks	3.5 cm	8 weeks	4.0 cm	10 weeks	4.9 cm
12 weeks	5.7 cm	14 weeks	6.3 cm		

1 Chart the growth of the shrew by making a bar line chart below.

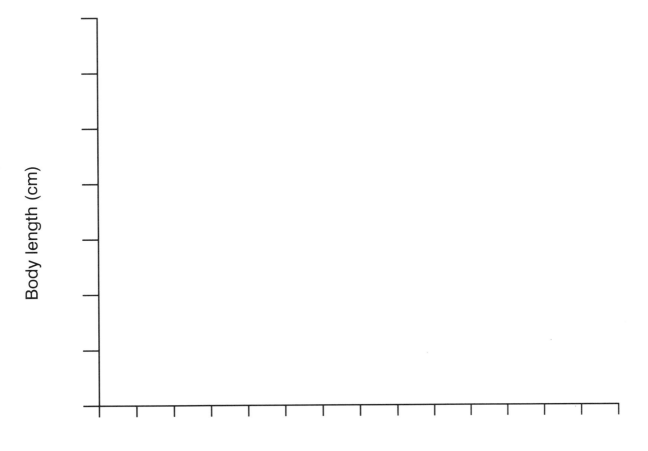

Body length (cm)

Number of weeks old

2 During which two weeks did the shrew grow most?

3 How can you tell by looking at the chart?

Maths Action Plans, Problems and Data Year 5/P6 © David Clemson and Wendy Clemson, Nelson Thornes Ltd, 2002

Goldfish chart

Almost every house in Acacia Avenue has a fishpond.
Some ponds have more goldfish in them than others:

10 ponds have 6 goldfish   7 ponds have 5 goldfish
3 ponds have 2 goldfish   8 ponds have 4 goldfish
1 pond has 3 goldfish   2 ponds have 1 goldfish

1 Make a bar line chart using this data.

[vertical axis label] Number of ponds

Number of goldfish

2 Do you think a line could be drawn to join the tops of the bar lines?
Would it make sense to do this? Talk about this with your classmates and
teacher.

Maths Action Plans, Problems and Data Year 5/P6 © David Clemson and Wendy Clemson, Nelson Thornes Ltd, 2002

Snacks data

Look at the information below, which shows the weekly sales of a range of snacks in a local shop.

	A	B	C	D	E	F	G	H	I	J
1		Salted	Chicken	Cheese & onion	Peanuts	Snax Bar	Jupiter Bar	Apples	Oranges	Bananas
2	Mon	£132.50	£123.75	£111.10	£75.25	£105.25	£118.70	£85.00	£35.00	£27.75
3	Tue	£122.45	£102.95	£121.75	£27.20	£98.50	£117.35	£37.50	£34.25	£37.75
4	Wed	£119.95	£109.95	£80.45	£12.50	£79.85	£79.95	£25.25	£37.75	£58.95
5	Thu	£74.75	£21.85	£125.45	£48.25	£29.95	£135.35	£77.25	£29.95	£87.95
6	Fri	£27.85	£0.00	£122.80	£35.25	£85.00	£116.95	£87.50	£92.50	£57.50
7										
8										

1 Use the SUM function to find the total takings for each item during the week.

2 Decide on a chart to best show which snack sold most.
Draw the chart on screen.

Write here your reasons for choosing this chart.

_____

_____

3 Write three more questions you could answer using the spreadsheet.
For each question write the kind of chart you would make.

_____

_____

_____

Using the SUM function

1   Prepare your spreadsheet using the data from the Resource Sheet you have been given.

2   Highlight the column or row you want to total.

3   Go to the top of the screen and click on Sum on the menu bar.

4   Your total appears at the bottom of the column or to the right of the row.

	A	B	C	D	E	F	G	H	I	J
1		Salted	Chicken	Cheese & Onion	Peanuts	Snax Bar	Jupiter Bar	Apples	Oranges	Bananas
2	Mon	£132.50	£123.75	£111.10	£75.25	£105.25	£118.70	£65.00	£35.00	£27.75
3	Tue	£122.45	£102.95	£121.75	£27.20	£98.50	£117.35	£37.50	£34.25	£37.75
4	Wed	£119.95	£109.95	£80.45	£12.50	£79.85	£79.95	£25.25	£37.75	£58.95
5	Thu	£74.75	£21.85	£125.45	£48.25	£29.95	£135.35	£77.25	£29.95	£67.95
6	Fri	£27.85	£0.00	£122.80	£35.25	£85.00	£116.95	£87.50	£92.50	£57.50
7										
8										

Make a chart or graph

1   Decide on the columns or rows for which you want to make a chart or graph. Highlight these by clicking and dragging.

2   Click on Chart at the top of the screen.

1   Choose where you want your labels.

2   The chart will be displayed as a bar chart.

Is this the best way to display this information? If you want a different type of graph or chart, then click one of these icons.

Bird watching

RESOURCE SHEET **49**

David is interested in bird watching.
He puts food on the bird table and then watches to see how often the robin visits the table in the next hour. He does this for 10 days.

Here is the tally of the robin's visits to the bird table.

Day	**Number of visits**
1	IIII
2	~~IIII~~ II
3	~~IIII~~ III
4	IIII
5	IIII
6	~~IIII~~ IIII
7	~~IIII~~ I
8	~~IIII~~ ~~IIII~~
9	III
10	~~IIII~~

1 What is the range of numbers of visits?

2 What is the mode?

3 David wants his friend William to see the robin on the bird table.
If William calls in as David is putting food on the bird table, how long do you think William will perhaps have to wait until he sees the robin?

Phone calls

Gemma likes phoning her friends. Dad is angry because he thinks she is spending too long on the phone. She says that she usually spends no longer than 5 minutes making a call. Is she right? Use the data to find out.

Friend	Length of call
Pat	3
Stacey	35
Raheed	6
Maggie	5
Ann	7
Stacey	14
Charlotte	10
Ann	5
Raheed	20
Joe	8
Pat	5
Charlotte	3

1 Do you think it is better for Gemma to use the range or the mode when talking to her Dad about the calls? Give your reasons for your answer.

_____

_____

2 Work out the range and mode. Which would you advise Gemma to use now?

_____

_____

Maths Action Plans, Problems and Data Year 5/P6 © David Clemson and Wendy Clemson, Nelson Thornes Ltd, 2002

Random numbers

11340

8

590

72

101

30

666

4824

45

20

272

60

1025

12

4

100110

5935

993

100

11340

70

415

36

25680

115

7850

Test results

These children have done two tests in school.

Here are their results.

Name	Maths test score	Science test score
Eric	49	56
Ron	68	61
Tamsin	62	54
Dylan	55	65
Morgan	42	67
Lucy	62	65
Finlay	76	59
Flora	51	65
Aaron	35	58
Alice	70	60

1 Find the range of the science test scores.

2 Find the mode of the science test scores.

3 What is the range of the maths test scores?

4 What is the mode of the maths test scores?

5 Which test do you think the children found easier? Explain your answer.

Maths Action Plans, Problems and Data Year 5/P6 © David Clemson and Wendy Clemson, Nelson Thornes Ltd, 2002

Cheese melts

Number cards

Cut out each number card.

17.45	88.71	☆10.67	85.21
15.02	44.81	81.47	45.45
38.30	34.60	35.65	57.96
35.55	80.35	27.63	92.81
51.35	71.66	71.97	87.56
67.43	35.25	71.07	18.51
97.88	42.97	71.51	33.95
57.76	19.78	86.11	99.01
35.27	38.76	81.80	74.53

Maths Action Plans, Problems and Data Year 5/P6 © David Clemson and Wendy Clemson, Nelson Thornes Ltd, 2002

Do it yourself!

Wood

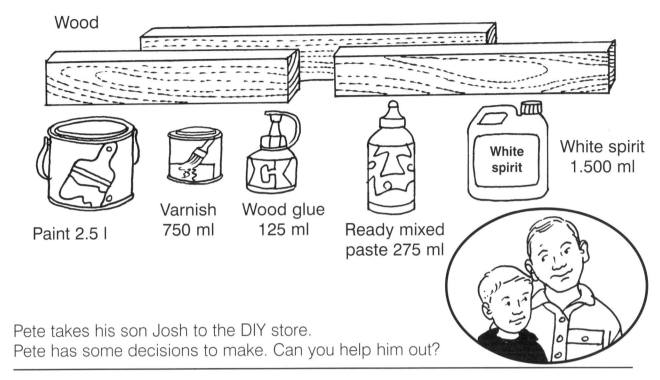

Paint 2.5 l

Varnish 750 ml

Wood glue 125 ml

Ready mixed paste 275 ml

White spirit

White spirit 1.500 ml

Pete takes his son Josh to the DIY store.
Pete has some decisions to make. Can you help him out?

1 Pete needs timber to make 3 shelves, each 1.35 m long.
   Timber comes in 1.5 m lengths.
   How many lengths should Pete buy?
   How much timber will be cut off each length?

2 Pete needs 1 litre of ready mixed paste.
   How many bottles of paste must he buy?
   If he uses 150 ml of paste from one bottle how much paste will be left in the
   bottle?

3 Pete buys 4 tins of white paint and 7 tins of green paint.
   How much white paint is that in total?
   How much more green paint than white paint?
   How much paint is there in 0.5 of a can?
   ... 0.2 of a can?

4 Plywood comes in a variety of thicknesses.
   Pete needs some half as thick again as 16 mm.
   How thick is that?
   What is the difference in thickness between 1.2 cm and 13.5 mm?

5 It takes 160 ml varnish to put one coat on a shelf.
   How many shelves can be given one coat by using a whole can of varnish?

Resource sheet 55

Get cooking!

Here are the ingredients for making gingerbread people.

350 g plain flour
5 ml   bicarbonate of soda
10 ml ground ginger
100 g butter
150 g soft brown sugar
60 ml golden syrup
1 egg

1 This recipe makes 20 biscuits.
Write out the ingredients to make:

30

50

3 If ¼ of the ginger is replaced with cinnamon, how much ginger and how much cinnamon will there be?

4 In a low fat, low sugar version of the biscuits the amounts of butter and sugar are halved. How much butter and sugar will there be in the recipe?

2 Susan and her friends are shopping and cooking for a juice and gingerbread party.

a) How many 300 ml drinks can they get from a 1 litre carton?

b) How many cartons do they need for 10 drinks?

c) How much flour will they need to make 40 biscuits?

d) If they make 3 batches of biscuits how much sugar will they use in all?

How much golden syrup?

How many eggs?

Multiplication grids

2	3	4	5	6	7	8	9	10	x
									10
									9
									8
									7
									6
									5
									4
									3
									2
2	3	4	5	6	7	8	9	10	x

2	3	4	5	6	7	8	9	10	x
								100	10
							81	90	9
						64	72	80	8
					49	56	63	70	7
				36	42	48	54	60	6
			25	30	35	40	45	50	5
		16	20	24	28	32	36	40	4
	9	12	15	18	21	24	27	30	3
4	6	8	10	12	14	16	18	20	2
2	3	4	5	6	7	8	9	10	x

Resource sheet 57

Maths Action Plans, Problems and Data Year 5/P6 © David Clemson and Wendy Clemson, Nelson Thornes Ltd, 2002

The cake factory

Doreen works in the cake factory.
Solve these problems related to Doreen's day.

1 This week Doreen is on the day shift from 08:00 until 16:30.
How many hours will she work each day?

How many hours will she work in total from Monday to Friday?

2 On Saturday Doreen usually works from 7:30 until 11:45. This week she takes half an hour off to go to the dentist.
How long does she work on Saturday?

3 Every month the factory has 2 days making wedding cakes. Doreen works 10 hours on both of these days.
She has 4 breaks of 25 minutes each.

How long does she take as break in each 10 hour shift?

What is her total break for both days?

4 Nightshift is 7 hours. When would Doreen finish each shift?
Here are the start times:
18:50
20:35
21:05

6 Doreen takes 10 minutes to wash and get into overalls before starting work. If she starts work at 06:15, what time must she arrive at the cake factory?

5 Chocolate cakes take 17 minutes along the assembly line after they leave the oven. If cakes leave the oven individually, how long will it take these cakes to complete assembly?
5 cakes
23 cakes
11 cakes

7 Icing a cakes takes Doreen 90 seconds (1 minute 30 seconds). How many cakes can she ice in 40 minutes and 30 seconds?

You may need a calculator for these.

Maths Action Plans, Problems and Data Year 5/P6 © David Clemson and Wendy Clemson, Nelson Thornes Ltd, 2002

The tide

A The tide comes in on the beach and goes out again twice in every 24 hours.

1 If high water is at 7:43 and then again at 20:03, how long is there between high tides?

2 If low water on another day is at 10:17 and then again at 23:04, what is the time between low tides?

B Now look at the tide table below and see if you can answer the questions.

Date	High water		Low water	
	Morning	Afternoon	Morning	Afternoon
Sunday	01.32	13.45	08.13	20.30
Monday	02.06	14.21	08.47	21.06
Tuesday	03.46	15.08	09.25	21.54
Wednesday	05.07	16.15	10.17	23.04

1 How long is it from high water to low water on Sunday morning?

2 How much later is the high tide on Tuesday morning than on Monday morning?

3 When is high water on Wednesday afternoon?

Maths Action Plans, Problems and Data Year 5/P6 © David Clemson and Wendy Clemson, Nelson Thornes Ltd, 2002

Railway timetable

Here is part of a railway timetable.

Mondays to Fridays						
Carlisle	1306	1315		1355	1455	
Penrith				1411	1513	
Oxenholme Lake District		1353		1437	1539	
Lancaster	1357	1410		1451	1557	1605
Blackpool North	1347	1354	1444	1454	1520	1553
Preston	1420	1434	1520	1530	1615	1630
Wigan North Western	1434		1534			1647

1 What time does the 13:06 from Carlisle reach Preston?

   How long does that journey take?

2 When does the 14:54 from Blackpool North reach Preston?

   What is that journey time?

3 Is it quicker to go from Carlisle to Penrith or Penrith to Oxenholme?

   How much quicker?

4 When is the next train to leave Lancaster after the 14:10 ?

5 If I just miss the 14:44 from Blackpool North for Wigan North Western, how long have I to wait for the next train?

6 Where did the 14:10 leaving Lancaster begin its journey?

Maths Action Plans, Problems and Data Year 5/P6 © David Clemson and Wendy Clemson, Nelson Thornes Ltd, 2002

Exchange rates (1)

Buying currency

When you travel to other countries you
need their money to use in shops
and cafés. Here is how much of
each currency you get for £1.
Use the table to answer the questions.

For £1   you get

1.6 Euros
1.5 US Dollars
190 yen
3 Australian Dollars

---

1 You are going to Disneyland USA.
You have saved £20. How much is that in US dollars?

---

2 You are going to France for your summer holiday.
You have been given £5 by each of your three Aunties
and you have saved £10 yourself.
How many Euros can you get?

---

3 You are going on a coach trip to the River Rhine in Germany.
How many Euros will you get for your £30 pocket money?

---

4 You are visiting an uncle in Tokyo, Japan where the currency is the yen.
You have £50 to spend.
How many yen can you expect when you change
the money?

---

5 Friends in Sydney want you to visit Australia.
They tell you to bring £85.
What is this in Australian dollars?

Exchange rates (2)

Buying and selling currency

When you visit many countries in the world you can buy their currency here before you go. When you return, you can sell your left-over foreign currency back to the bank, travel agent or other exchange bureau. You don't always get the same price, though.

Here is a table which shows the buying price and selling price for some currencies. Use the table to help you to answer the questions.

Remember that the figures here are what £1 will buy or what you need to get £1 when you sell.

Country/currency	Buy	Sell
(Europe) Euro	1.6	1.7
US dollar	1.4	1.5
Swiss franc	2.3	2.6
Australian dollar	2.5	3

1 How many Euros could you get for £50?

2 If you had 34 Euros left after your holiday how many pounds would you get?

3 You buy 30.8 US dollars. How much did they cost in pounds sterling?

4 You have only 4.5 dollars left after your trip to New York. How much is that in pounds sterling if you sell them?

5 You go skiing in Switzerland. You have saved £45 for spending money. How many Swiss francs can you buy?

6 On your return from Switzerland you get £2 back for your Swiss francs. How many did you have left?

7 If you buy £50 worth of Australian dollars and then sell back your remaining 22.5 dollars, what did you spend while you were there?

How much is left in pounds and pence?

Maths Action Plans, Problems and Data Year 5/P6 © David Clemson and Wendy Clemson, Nelson Thornes Ltd, 2002

Percentage challenge

Work out the answer to these challenges
and write them in your books.

1 When 100 people went to a concert, 60 of them really enjoyed it but the others
   did not. What percentage didn't enjoy themselves?

2 A fifth of a class of 25 children have a cold.
   What percentage is that?

3 Your family wants to buy a new TV. The one you want costs £350
   but isn't in stock. You have to leave a deposit of 25%.
   How much is that?

4 A local hi-fi and games shop is having a 20% off everything sale.
   How much would the following items costs in the sale?
   Fill in the last column.

Item	Price	Sale Price
CD	£14	
Computer game	£40	
Video	£15	
Tapes	£7	

5 A shop has a notice which says "25% off *or* buy two and get one free".
   If you bought three pencil cases with pencils for £5 each which would be
   the best buy – the "percentage off' or the 'two and a free one"?

Maths Action Plans, Problems and Data Year 5/P6 © David Clemson and Wendy Clemson, Nelson Thornes Ltd, 2002

Running your own business

Imagine you own a shop. You buy things for your shop which you have to sell at a profit. Work out how much you will sell these things for.

---

1 Good quality plastic clipboards cost you £4.
You want to make 20% profit. How much will you
sell them for?

---

2 Packets of A4 note paper cost you £3.90. You sell them
with 10% profit. How much do you sell them for?

---

3 You have 80 calendars. Before Christmas you sell 50%
of them for £5. In January you sell another 25% of them
for £4. Then you have to sell the remainder at £3.50.
How much did you collect altogether?

---

4 If the calendars cost you £300, how much profit
did you make in pounds?

Spinners

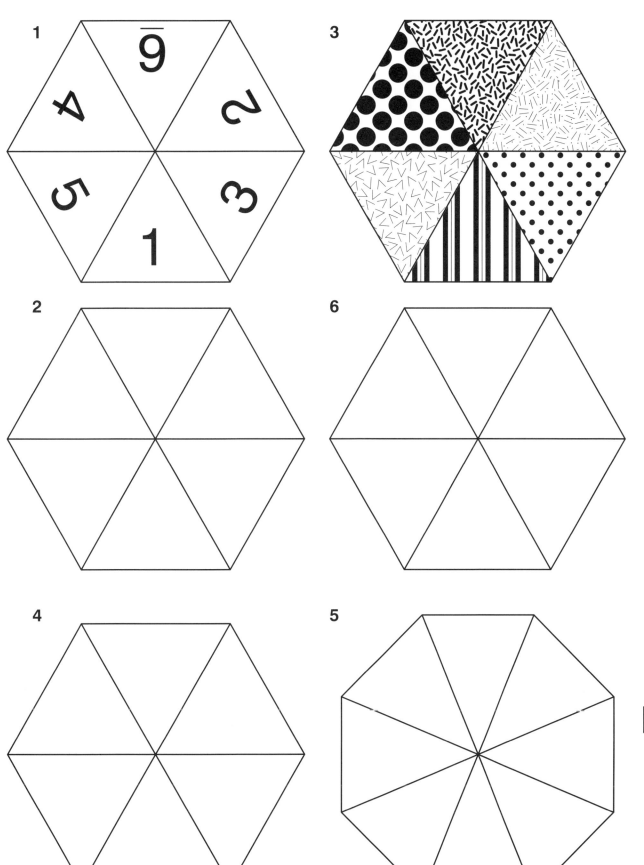

1

9
4
5
1
3
2

3

2

6

4

5

General resource sheet A

Centimetre squares

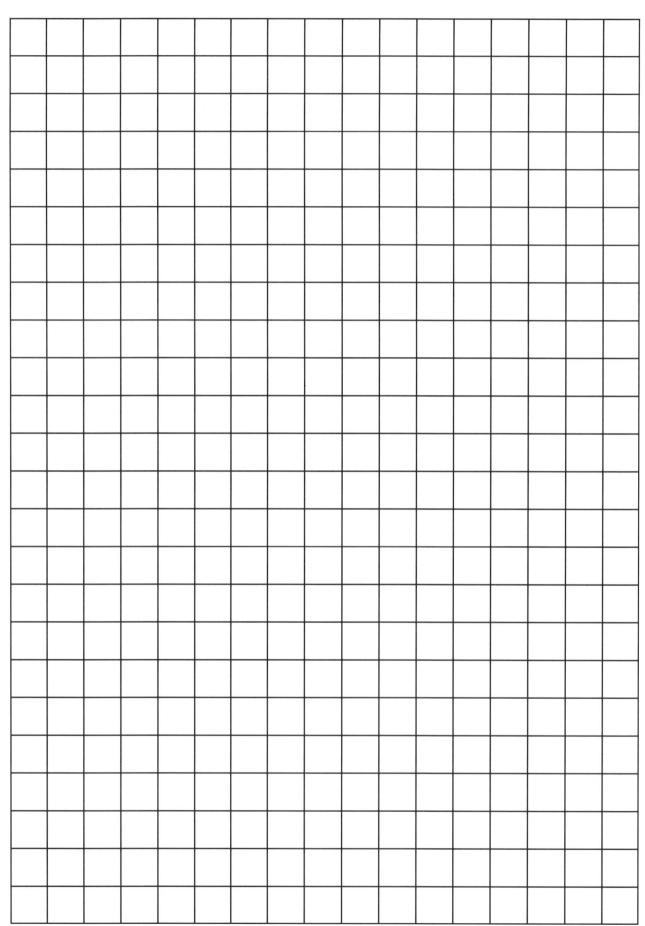

Half centimetre squares

GENERAL RESOURCE SHEET **C**

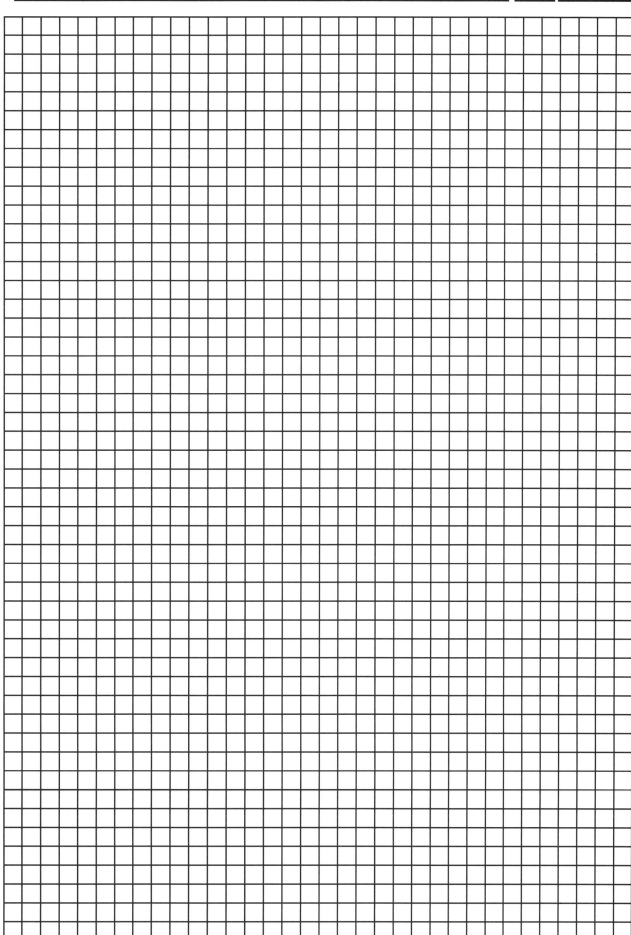

General resource sheet C

Maths Action Plans, Problems and Data Year 5/P6 © David Clemson and Wendy Clemson, Nelson Thornes Ltd, 2002